Popular Complete Smart Series

Complete
ScienceSmart®

Grade **3**

William Young

Credits

Photos (Front Cover "satellite dish" David Hughes/123RF.com, "gears" alex_star/123RF.com, "jet plane" Lars Christenen/123RF.com.
Back Cover "girl on left"/123RF.com, "boy" Jose Manuel Gelpi Diaz/123RF.com, "girl in middle"/123RF.com,
"girl on right" Paul Hakimata/123RF.com, "memo board" Sandra Van Der Steen/123RF.com, "children"/123RF.com.)

ISBN: 978-1-897457-75-7

Table of Contents

Section 1

Understanding Life Systems

Students will investigate a variety of plants and study their basic structure and characteristics. They will also learn about how plants interact with animals and how different plants pollinate and disperse seeds. The growth of plants and the germination of seeds will also be discussed. Students will also study how plants adapt to their environments and how humans make use of plants for food and products. Moreover, they will explore the impacts of human activities and environmental conditions on plant life.

ISBN: 978-1-897457-75-7

Section 2

Understanding Structures and Mechanisms

Students will understand that both humans and animals build structures and need their structures to be strong and stable. They will investigate the factors that affect a structure's strength and stability, and learn to identify the centre of gravity in structures. They will apply their knowledge to design and build strong and stable structures using suitable materials. Moreover, they will study the different types of bridges, and see how structures affect our society.

ISBN: 978-1-897457-75-7

Table of Contents

Section 3 Understanding Matter and Energy

Students will develop an understanding that there are two basic types of forces that cause movement: contact force and non-contact force. They will learn about ways in which forces cause objects to move and that movement is caused by unbalanced forces. They will explore what friction is, how it occurs, and how much of it is required in different activities. In addition, students will examine devices that use forces to create controlled movement.

ISBN: 978-1-897457-75-7

Understanding Earth and Space Systems

Students will learn about soil and identify the different types of soil. They will understand that soil is an essential source of life and it provides nutrients for many living things. Students will also learn that soil not only provides food and water for plants, but it can also be used by humans to make things. When exploring the importance of soil, students will also study the process of composting and learn how to prevent soil erosion.

ISBN: 978-1-897457-75-7

ISBN: 978-1-897457-75-7

Section 1

Understanding
Life Systems

ISBN: 978-1-897457-75-7

1 Plants and Their Needs

There are many different kinds of plants in the world. Have you noticed any of their characteristics? In this unit, you will learn about what plants are, what they need to grow and live, and how these needs are similar to what animals need.

After completing this unit, you will

- understand that plants are living things.
- know how plants are different from animals.
- know what plants need to live and grow.

> *Trees grow throughout their lives, so I am sure my tree will grow taller than I am one day.*

characteristic: need water

characteristic: feature that helps us identify something

ISBN: 978-1-897457-75-7

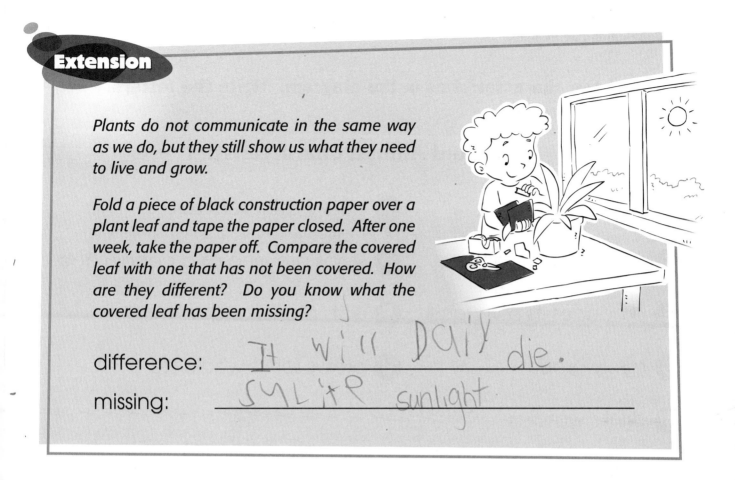

Plants do not communicate in the same way as we do, but they still show us what they need to live and grow.

Fold a piece of black construction paper over a plant leaf and tape the paper closed. After one week, take the paper off. Compare the covered leaf with one that has not been covered. How are they different? Do you know what the covered leaf has been missing?

difference: ___It will Daiy die.___

missing: ___suLite sunlight.___

A. Complete the diagram with the given words. Then write an example of your own.

living things

PLAnt — OAk tree

my example — SuFLAWen

ANimals — sPuinel

my example — Wolf

oak tree
animals
plants
squirrel

B. Sort the characteristics in the diagram. Write the letters.

Plant and Animal Characteristics

A needs water

C stays in one place

E produces its own food

G rarely green

I drinks water

J travels around

K grows

L likes sunshine

M often green

B gets water from soil

D stops growing at a certain age

F eats plants and animals

H grows for its whole life

Characteristics of...

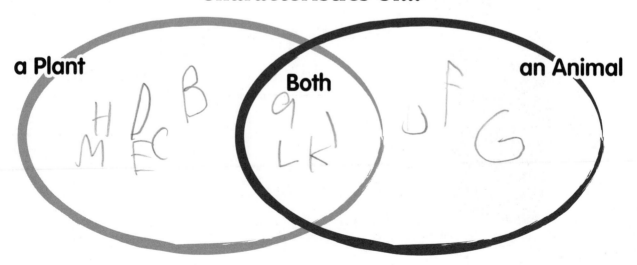

a Plant   **Both**   **an Animal**

H D B   9 I   J F
M E C   L K   G

   ISBN: 978-1-897457-75-7

C. **Fill in the missing letters to see what plants need. Then complete the poem and fill in the blanks.**

Plants Need...

- ☼ _l_ _i_ ght
- ᵔᵔᵔ ai_r_
- ⬦ w_a_ter
- ⟋ sp_a_ce
- ⌇ war_m_ _t_ _h_
- ⬭ fo_o_ _d_

When the forest is crowded
When space is tight
Trees grow up, not out
Because they all need 1. _light_.

People and plants
There's a need we share
They don't breathe like we do
But we all need 2. _air_.

It doesn't matter
If it's colder or hotter
To move food and waste through
Plants need 3. _water_.

Plants in cold climates are small and fewer. Plants need 4. _warmth_ to grow.

Plants do not eat like animals do. They make their own 5. _food_.

ISBN: 978-1-897457-75-7

D. Read the passage. Then answer the questions.

Even Cacti Need Water

Almost all cacti live in environments where it rains very little. Since they are designed to store water, they are able to survive in these dry, hot areas. Cacti come in many shapes and sizes, but most have some water storage and collection features in common.

One feature is a thick, waxy stem covered with spines that can store lots of water. Some cacti even have stems that can absorb water from the air, much like roots absorb water from the ground. Another feature is prickly spines, which protect cacti from animals that want to eat or get water from them, and provide some shade for cacti stems. Finally, most cacti have amazing roots that grow quickly after a rainfall, spreading wide and shallow in the ground to collect as much water as possible.

ISBN: 978-1-897457-75-7

1. Name the parts that help a cactus survive in dry, hot areas. Then describe the functions of each part.

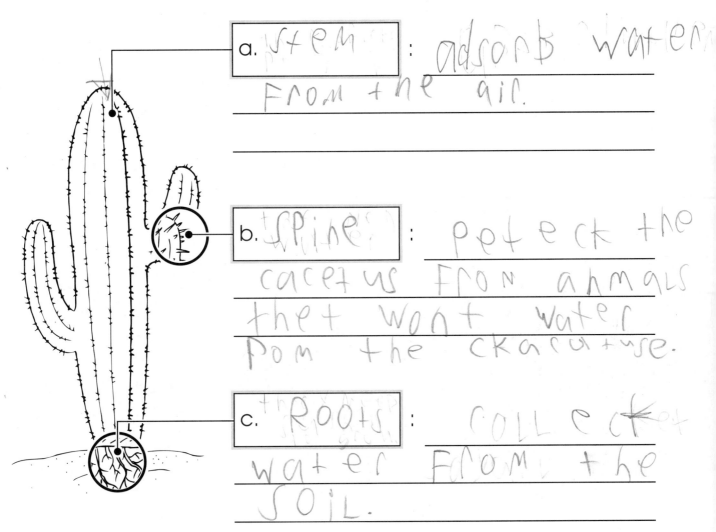

a. stem : adsorb water from the air.

b. spine : poteck the cacetus fron ahmals thet wont water pom the ckaratuse.

c. Roots : collect water from the soil.

2. Do this simple experiment to see how a cactus's waxy stem helps it retain water.

1 Wet 2 pieces of paper towels and place each on a plate.

wet paper towel

2 Place a piece of paper over one plate and a piece of wax paper over the other plate.

3 Wait a few days.

Result

It wo hit onB20B the wad beau e it wax and wax Das not utBOB water

ISBN: 978-1-897457-75-7

2 Parts of Plants

Each part of a plant has a purpose that helps the plant survive and grow. In this unit, you will learn the names of the main parts of plants and what they do. You will see that the parts of different kinds of plants have different characteristics.

After completing this unit, you will

- know the main parts of most plants and understand what they do.
- know that the parts of different kinds of plants have different characteristics.

Mom, they don't look the same, but they are all flowers!

taproot

Vocabulary

bark: a tree trunk's protective covering

taproot: a single root growing downwards

fibrous roots: spreading roots

 ISBN: 978-1-897457-75-7

We can touch the bark, but we shouldn't rip it from the tree.

Extension

Like skin for humans, trees have bark as their outermost layer to protect themselves. Take a walk around your neighbourhood to get a closer look at the bark of some trees. You will find that the bark of different tree species has different features and colours. Make a chart to record your findings.

Tree...	in my backyard	at school
texture (rough/smooth)		
colour		

A. Circle the correct words. Then fill in the blanks.

Functions of Roots

dandelion

- absorb **water / soil** and **worms / minerals**

- **anchor / move** the plant in the soil

Two Major Kinds of Roots

monocot

- taproot: a **single / double** root growing downwards

  e.g. _____

- fibrous root: **anchoring / spreading** roots

  e.g. _____

B. Fill in the blanks to describe the basic functions of a plant's stem and leaves, and the extra functions of each stem. Then describe the characteristics of the leaves in your own words.

winds   covered   thorns   food   water   nutrients

Stems and Leaves

1. All stems move _____ up and down the plant.

2. Most leaves use sunlight to make _____ .

3. **stem:**   stores _____ and makes food

    leaves: _____

4. **stem:**   protects the plants with its sharp
    _____

    leaves: _____

5. **stem:**   _____ around its support as it
    grows

    leaves: _____

6. **stem:**   _____ in a protective layer of
    bark

    leaves: _____

C. Write the names and functions of different parts of a flower. Then complete the sentences with the words in bold.

Parts of a Flower

ovary   petal   pistil   sepal   stamen
flower   seeds   ovary   base

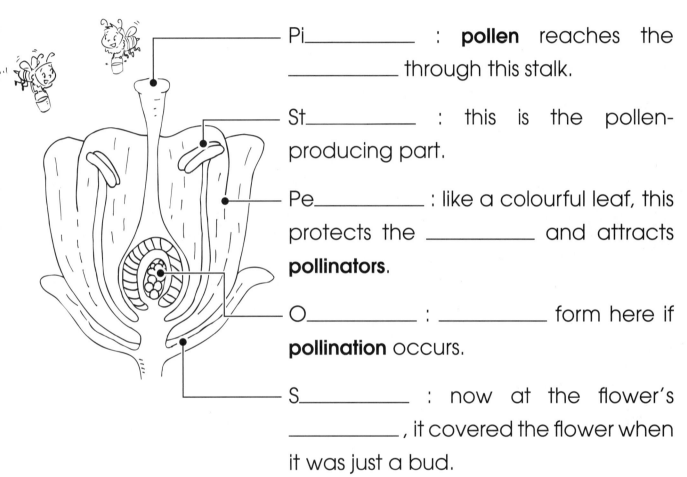

Pi_____ : **pollen** reaches the _____ through this stalk.

St_____ : this is the pollen-producing part.

Pe_____ : like a colourful leaf, this protects the _____ and attracts **pollinators**.

O_____ : _____ form here if **pollination** occurs.

S_____ : now at the flower's _____ , it covered the flower when it was just a bud.

How Flowers Make Seeds

_____ is the delivery of _____ from one flower's stamen to another flower's pistil. _____ carry pollen from flower to flower. They are most often insects, birds, bats, or the wind.

D.   Read the passage. Then answer the questions.

Trees:
Broadleaf and Conifer

We all know what trees look like. However, do you know what makes a tree a tree? To be a tree, a woody plant must be at least 3 metres tall at maturity* and have a minimum diameter of 10 centimetres. If a woody plant does not reach this size at maturity, it is referred to as a shrub.

There are two types of trees: broadleaf and conifer. Broadleaf trees typically lose their wide, flat leaves after the leaves change colour in the fall. They produce flowers, though their flowers are not always easy to see. Examples of broadleaf trees are sugar maples, birch, and oak. Conifers have needle-like leaves and produce seed cones. They are usually evergreen. Examples of conifers are cedar, pine, and spruce trees.

Broadleaf

Conifer

*maturity: when a tree is fully developed

     ISBN: 978-1-897457-75-7

1. Fill in the blanks.

   Trees are a _____ plant. If a woody plant reaches

   a height of _____ and is a minimum of _____

   in diameter at maturity, it is a _____ . Otherwise, it is

   referred to as a _____ .

2. Identify each tree as "broadleaf" or "conifer".

   _____   _____   _____

3. Write any two characteristics of each type of tree. Then
   give two examples of each.

   Broadleaf Trees

   Characteristics:

   _____

   _____

   Examples:

   _____

   Conifer Trees

   Characteristics:

   _____

   _____

   Examples:

   _____

3 Plant Survival

There are many ways that different plants survive and thrive. In this unit, you will see that plants have different ways of being pollinated, of dispersing their seeds, and of adapting to their environment.

After completing this unit, you will

- know different methods of pollination and seed dispersal.

- understand that plants adapt to their environments.

Where you live, many kinds of plants thrive, but in the Arctic, only a few can survive.

seeds dispersed

Vocabulary

adaptation: a change to suit an environment

disperse: spread out

biome: an area of plants and animals and their habitats

ISBN: 978-1-897457-75-7

Extension

No plant moves as quickly as the slowest animal, but plants do move! Sunflower buds follow the sun across the sky, and vines search for supports around which to wind. Ask your parents for two small vine plants. Then set up the plants with the sticks as shown. After a few weeks, check the plants to see how they have grown. Record your observations.

2 sticks placed vertically

2 sticks placed vertically
2 sticks placed horizontally

A. Circle the correct words to describe the two major types of pollination. Then write the letters that go with the correct flower examples.

Animal Pollination

Flowers: have **strong / no** scents

e.g. ( )   have **bitter / sweet** nectar

have **bright / dull** colours

pollinated by **animals / plants**

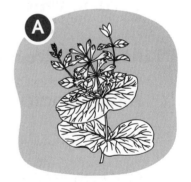

A

Wind Pollination

Flowers: are **big / small**

e.g. ( )   have **strong / no** scents

are **colourful / not colourful**

pollinated by **animals / wind**

B

ISBN: 978-1-897457-75-7

B. Fill in the blanks to show how plants adapt themselves to their environments. Then write the letters to match the pictures with the correct descriptions.

stores   turns   defends   appears

Plant Adaptations

- _____ towards light; e.g. _____

- _____ water in its stem; e.g. _____

- _____ itself against animals; e.g. _____

- _____ attractive to pollinators; e.g. _____

C. Fill in the blanks to complete the descriptions about the adaptations needed for plants to live in different biomes. Then write in which biome the plant in the picture belongs.

Plants in Different Biomes

top   float   ground

1. **Arctic Tundra**

   Plants grow in clumps for protection, and grow close to the _____ .

2. **Rainforest**

   Plants can grow on _____ of others to better reach the light.

3. **Aquatic**

   Leaves _____ in order to get sunlight.

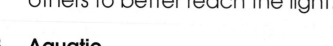

4.

ISBN: 978-1-897457-75-7

D. Match the plants with their methods of dispersal. Write the plant names. Then answer the questions.

Seed Dispersal

By Water:

1. _____

2. _____

By Animal:

3. _____

4. _____

By Wind:

5. _____

6. _____

blackberry

dandelion

mangrove

maple

burdock

coconut

Which method of seed dispersal would be best for...

7. a plant on a small island?

   _____

8. a plant in a dense forest?   _____

9. a plant in an open field?   _____

ISBN: 978-1-897457-75-7

E. Read the passage. Then answer the questions.

How Plants Disperse Seeds

Plants make use of wind, water, and animals to disperse seeds. Some also use gravity: a plant's heavy fruit simply falls to the ground and rolls away or breaks apart, such as the fruit of the calabash vine and the European beech tree. There are some plants that use yet another method. It is called mechanical dispersal: the sun dries out a plant's seed pods and the dry pods split or pop open, flinging the seeds far and wide. An example of this is the pea plant. When a pod dries out, its two seams split and release its seeds. Another example is the sandbox tree. Its small, pumpkin-shaped fruit "explodes", popping open to fling seeds up to 45 metres from the tree.

   ISBN: 978-1-897457-75-7

1. Name the methods of seed dispersal mentioned in the passage. For each method, provide an example of a plant.

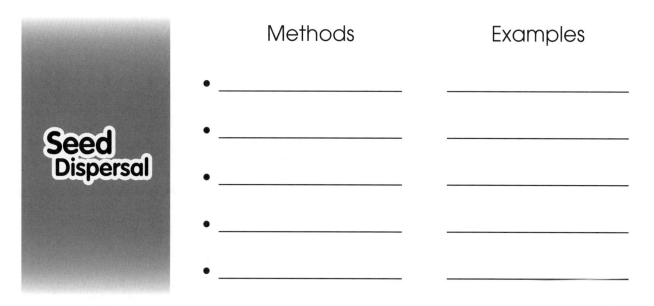

Methods   Examples

- _____   _____
- _____   _____
- _____   _____
- _____   _____
- _____   _____

2. Describe how a pea plant disperses its seeds. Then check the picture that goes with your description.

Seed Dispersal of a Pea Plant

_____

_____

_____

_____

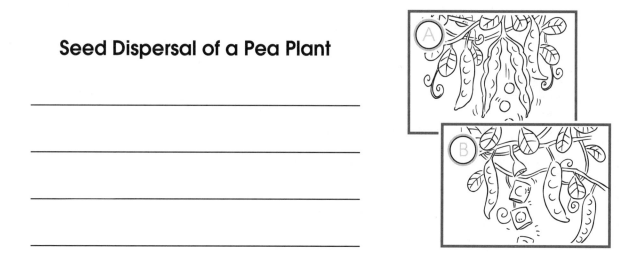

3. Passion fruit vines rely on gravity to disperse their seeds. What do you think about the weight of their fruit? Explain your idea.

_____

_____

ISBN: 978-1-897457-75-7

Experiment

Introduction

A plant's stem holds its leaves up to the light. The stem is also said to carry water and nutrients from the roots to the leaves and flowers, but this is not easy to see. How do we know for sure that water moves up the stem?

Hypothesis

Check one.

(A) Water moves up a plant's stem.

(B) Water does not move up a plant's stem.

Materials

• *a white carnation*
• *a glass of water*
• *food colouring*
• *scissors*

Steps

1. Cut the bottom end of the flower stem so that it is freshly cut.

2. Put a few drops of food colouring in the glass of water.

3. Put the carnation in the coloured water.

If you don't have a carnation, you can use a piece of leafy celery instead.

ISBN: 978-1-897457-75-7

4. Observe it for three days and record your observations.

Observations

Draw and colour the pictures to show your observations.

Start	After 1 day	After 3 days

Result

What happened to the carnation? Explain.

_____

_____

Conclusion

The hypothesis was: _____

_____

My experiment _____ the
hypothesis.   supported/did not support

4 Plant Growth

Seeds need special conditions to germinate and grow into plants. In this unit, you will learn about germination and see how a seed grows into a mature plant.

After completing this unit, you will

- know what germination is.
- understand the conditions needed for germination.
- know about the life cycles of some plants.

Let's see how a small seed becomes a giant tree!

seed germination

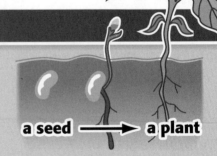

a seed ⟶ a plant

Vocabulary

germination: the process of sprouting from a seed into a seedling

life cycle: a series of stages of development

shoot: early growth from a germinating seed

ISBN: 978-1-897457-75-7

When seeds are dispersed, they may land in the soil downwards, upwards, or even sideways. Have you ever wondered why a plant never grows upside down?

Seeds have a special property to ensure that roots grow downwards and stems grow upwards. The seed's roots are sensitive to gravity and are pulled down. Since plants need sunlight to grow, stems must find their way out of the ground. This is why a plant always grows right side up.

A. Put the pictures in order from 1 to 3. Then fill in the blanks to complete the descriptions.

How a Seed Germinates

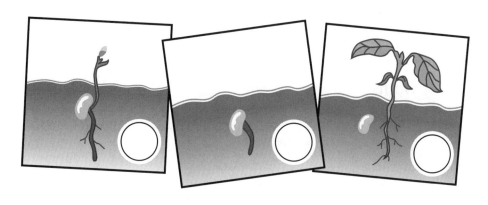

germination
leaves
root
shoot
water

- First, the seed sends a _____ downwards into the soil to take in _____ .

- Next, it sends a _____ upwards to get sunlight.

- Once the baby plant grows _____ , it can start making its own food using sunlight. The _____ process is complete.

ISBN: 978-1-897457-75-7

B. Look at each experiment. Circle the word that tells whether or not a certain condition is needed for germination. Then fill in the blanks and unscramble the letters.

Conditions Needed for Germination   Result

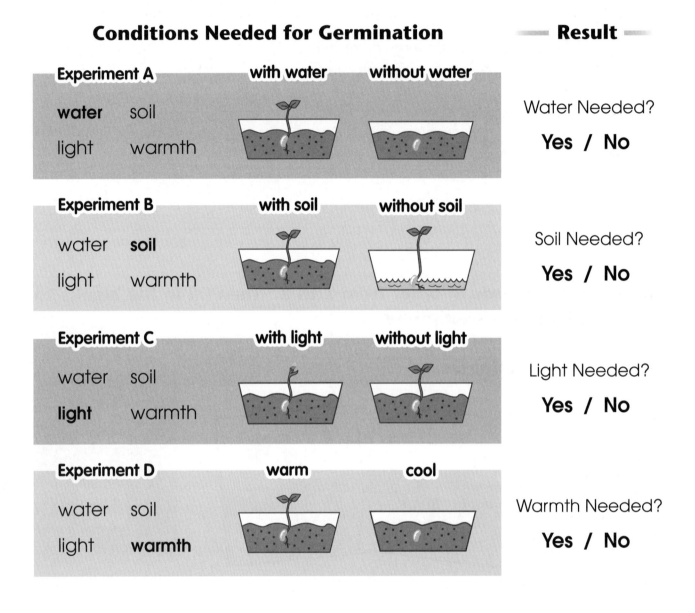

Experiment A

water   soil

light   warmth

with water   without water

Water Needed?

Yes / No

Experiment B

water   **soil**

light   warmth

with soil   without soil

Soil Needed?

Yes / No

Experiment C

water   soil

light   warmth

with light   without light

Light Needed?

Yes / No

Experiment D

water   soil

light   **warmth**

warm   cool

Warmth Needed?

Yes / No

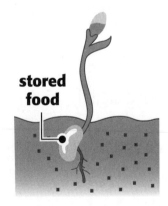

stored food

Seeds need _____ and _____ to germinate. They use their stored _____ for energy to grow. Once their

ofod

energy is depleted, the green seedlings make their own food using _____ .

hgusnlit

C. Fill in the blanks to complete the descriptions of the plant life cycle.

| leaves | germinates | life cycle | soil |
| tree | flowers | fruit | seed |

The Life Cycle of a *Cherry Tree*

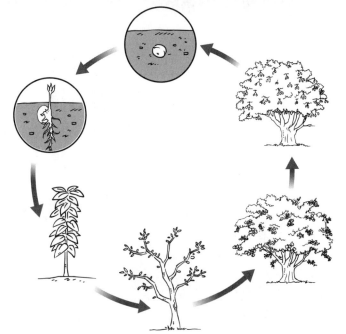

1. The seed is buried in well-watered _____ .

2. The seed _____ and becomes a baby plant.

3. Sunlight helps the stem grow _____ .

4. The plant becomes a small _____ .

5. When the tree is mature, it has _____ . Then the flowers will fall off and the tree will produce _____ .

6. The fruit containing a _____ will fall from the tree in the fall.

Then a new seed will find its way into the soil.
The 7. _____ will start all over again.

ISBN: 978-1-897457-75-7

D. **Read the passage. Then answer the questions.**

Bulbs:
the Underground
Stems

A bulb is a modified stem that develops underground as a bundle of stored nutrients for a flowering plant. Onions and garlic are examples of edible bulbs.

Tulips and lilies are common spring flowers* that can grow from bulbs. These plants "fill" the bulb with nutrients as the above-ground part of the plant withers in the summer. The bulb stores the nutrients underground through the fall and winter. Early in the spring, water and warm weather "wake" the bulb up, and roots and a bud begin to grow, fed by the bulb's nutrients. These plants produce seeds if they are pollinated, and new plants grow from the seeds. Seeds take years to grow flowers, while bulbs grow flowers every year. This is why gardeners prefer to plant bulbs to seeds for tulips and lilies; they wait for only a few seasons, not many years, to enjoy the blooms.

*spring flowers: flowers that bloom in the spring

ISBN: 978-1-897457-75-7

1. Put the pictures in order from 1 to 5 to show how a bulb grows.

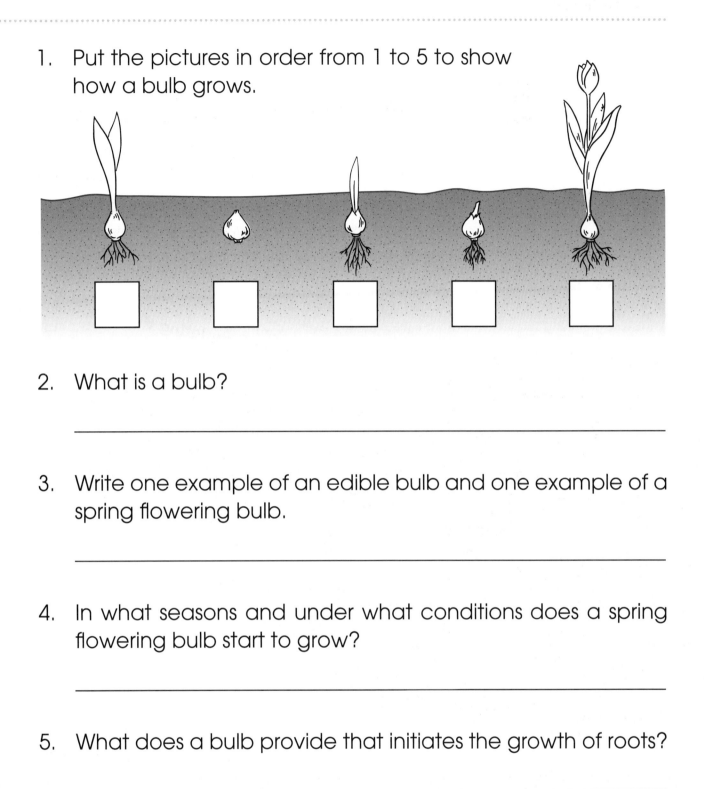

2. What is a bulb?

   _____

3. Write one example of an edible bulb and one example of a spring flowering bulb.

   _____

4. In what seasons and under what conditions does a spring flowering bulb start to grow?

   _____

5. What does a bulb provide that initiates the growth of roots?

   _____

6. Why do gardeners prefer planting bulbs to sowing seeds for tulips?

   _____

   _____

5 How We Use Plants

We use plants for all sorts of things in our everyday lives. In this unit, you will explore two important uses all animals have for plants: food and oxygen. You will also see how we use plants for many other things.

logs as shelter

apple as food

cotton as clothing

straw as container

After completing this unit, you will

- understand that plants are the ultimate supply of food for all animals.

- know that we eat different plant parts and grow plants in different places.

- know some non-food uses for plants.

Fruit — seed

seed

seed

Vocabulary

sap: liquid that carries nutrients within a plant

fruit: the ripened ovary or ovaries of a plant; holds the seed or seeds

ISBN: 978-1-897457-75-7

Plants need animals as much as animals need plants! How do plants need animals? Look at the list of things animals do that benefit plants.

Things that Animals Do that Benefit Plants:

1. *Animals carry pollen from flower to flower. (pollination)*

2. *Animals carry seeds from one place to another. (seed dispersal)*

3. *Animal waste enriches soil, making it nutritious for plants.*

> *I'm sorry that it stinks, but it does wonders for plants.*

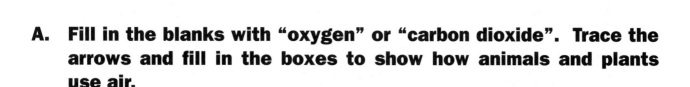

A. Fill in the blanks with "oxygen" or "carbon dioxide". Trace the arrows and fill in the boxes to show how animals and plants use air.

Animals breathe in o_____ and breathe out c_____ .

Plants use c_____ and release o_____ .

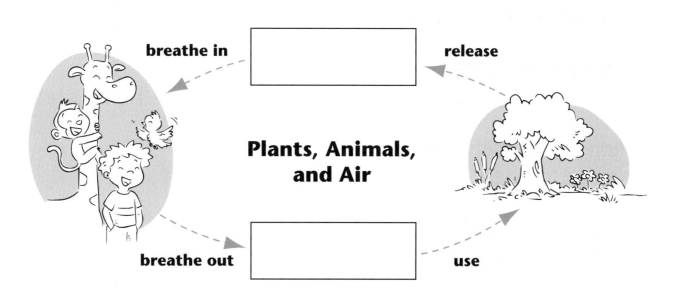

breathe in

release

Plants, Animals, and Air

breathe out

use

B. **Write which plant part each group of foods comes from.**

seed   sap   leaf   fruit   stem   root

_____

_____

_____

[   ]

[   ]

_____

C. **Draw lines to show where we grow our food.**

Fruit trees grow in rows.   •

Plants are protected from cool weather.   •

Plants and animals are reared for food.   •

People can grow their own food in their yard.   •

• greenhouse

• home garden

• farm

• orchard

   ISBN: 978-1-897457-75-7

D. **We use plants in different areas of our lives. Write the areas and sort the things into the correct areas. Then give one more example for each area and answer the question.**

Areas	Things
medicine food clothing shelter	rubber (from sap) garlic (natural antibiotic) bread wooden staircase paper

1. _____

- furniture
- wallpaper
- _____
- _____

2. _____

- ginseng
  (lowers blood pressure)
- peppermint
  (calms upset stomach)
- _____
- _____

3. _____

- peanut butter
- herbs and spices
- _____
- _____

4. _____

- rayon (from wood pulp)
- linen (from flax plant)
- _____
- _____

5.   **others**

- canoes (tree bark)
- firewood
- _____
- _____

6.   Write two ways animals use plants. Then give one specific example for each.

- _____
- _____

E. Read the passage. Then answer the questions.

Using Corn:
Then and Now

Historically, many Aboriginal societies in the Americas farmed corn, and it had many uses. Cornmeal, flour made from ground corn, was used to make bread, pudding, and syrup. Whole kernels were used to make soup and popcorn. Corn husks were used to make masks, bags, baskets, floor and bed mats, dolls, and moccasins. Corncobs were used for fuel.

Today, corn is one of the most farmed crops in the world. It is a major food source for both people and livestock. Its kernels are burned for fuel and it is processed to make a fuel called ethanol. Corn is used as environmentally friendly insulation for houses and as a material in tires. It can even be used to make a fabric called rayon.

1. Complete the table to list the uses of corn in the past and the present mentioned in the passage.

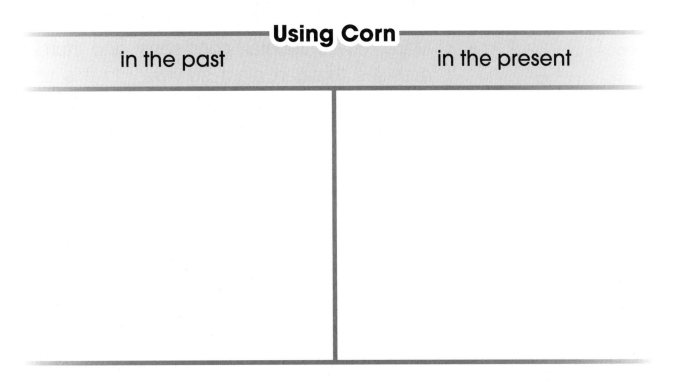

Using Corn	
in the past	in the present

2. Fill in the blanks with the words in bold to complete the diagram.

A corn plant's tall, rigid **stalk** grows to 2 to 3 metres and supports each **ear** of corn. An ear of corn is the cob and its protective covering, the **husk**. The **kernels**, which are the corn plant's seeds, are attached to the cob.

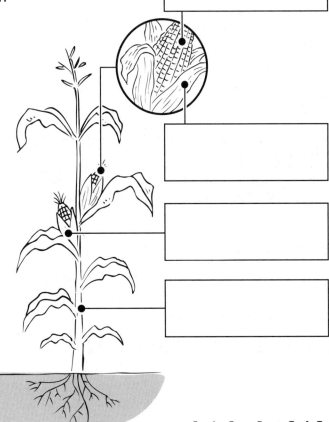

6 Protecting Plants

Many environmental conditions and human activities threaten plant survival. In this unit, you will see what some of these conditions and activities are and how they affect plants. You will see why it is important to protect plants and know the role of a botanist.

purple loosestrife

After completing this unit, you will

- understand that human activities and environmental conditions impact plant life.

- know what a botanist does.

While it looks pretty, purple loosestrife is very invasive! That's why we can see it everywhere.

foxglove
(native to Ontario)

Vocabulary

botanist: a scientist who studies plants

invasive: tends to spread beyond where it is wanted

native: original to an area

non-native: not native to an area

ISBN: 978-1-897457-75-7

Native plants are the plants that occur naturally in an area. Each province or territory in Canada has native plants that it considers special. Look at the official flower of each province or territory. Do you know why it is a symbol of your province or territory?

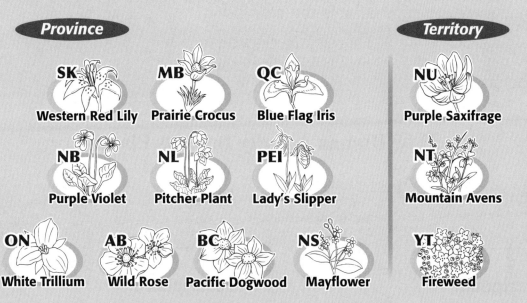

Province

SK — Western Red Lily
MB — Prairie Crocus
QC — Blue Flag Iris
NB — Purple Violet
NL — Pitcher Plant
PEI — Lady's Slipper
ON — White Trillium
AB — Wild Rose
BC — Pacific Dogwood
NS — Mayflower

Territory

NU — Purple Saxifrage
NT — Mountain Avens
Y.T. — Fireweed

A. Check the correct conditions.

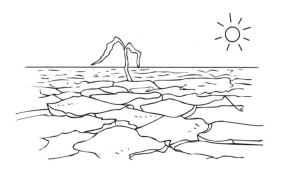

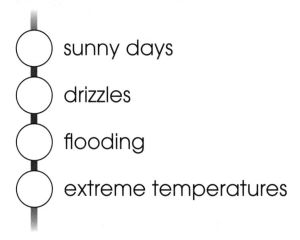

Environmental Conditions that Threaten Plant Life

- ◯ sunny days
- ◯ drizzles
- ◯ flooding
- ◯ extreme temperatures

- ◯ drought
- ◯ rain
- ◯ wildfires
- ◯ tornadoes

B. Name or write about the human activity. Then describe the impact the activity has on plant life.

Activity	Description	Impact
• farming • construction • gardening • factories	• Invasive, non-native plants are planted. • Forests are cleared to make fields for crops.	• loss of marsh habitat • trees die

How Human Activity Impacts Plants

Activity:

_____

Description:

_____

_____

Impact:

loss of forest habitat

Activity:

_____

Description:

A marsh is filled for a new development.

Impact:

_____

Activity:

_____

Description:

Air pollution causes acid rain to fall on trees.

Impact:

_____

Activity:

_____

Description:

_____

_____

Impact:

no room for native plants

ISBN: 978-1-897457-75-7

C. Check the correct circles. Write one more reason why it is important to save plants.

The Importance of **Saving Plants**

- (A) They form animal habitats.
- (B) They are our source of food.
- (C) They protect against soil erosion.
- (D) They are our source of soil.
- (✔) _____

D. The children are role-playing as botanists. Fill in the blanks with "plants" or "fruit" to complete the concerns botanists can have. Then unscramble the letters.

What 2._____ can we grow to prevent flooding?

How can we grow bigger, better 1._____ ?

Why are some of the 3._____ in this ecosystem dying?

4. All botanists study _____ , but the reasons why they
   tpsaln

   study them can be _____ .
   fdtiferne

E.   Read the passage. Then answer the questions.

Gardens:
Good for the Environment!

Gardening with plants native to an area is good for the environment. Native plants support the insects, birds, and other animals in a habitat, and they often do not need to be watered or fertilized, as they are well suited to their environment. They are also great for the community because they can teach people about their natural heritage. Here are some examples of plants native to Toronto:

Wild Columbine

(blooms from May to June)

- flowers are red with yellow centres

- grows to be 10 to 50 cm tall

- needs moist soil and some shade

Black-eyed Susan

(blooms from June to July)

- flowers are yellow with dark brown centres

- grows to be up to 50 cm tall

- needs dry to moist soil and lots of sun

ISBN: 978-1-897457-75-7

1. Colour the two plants native to Toronto. Then complete the table.

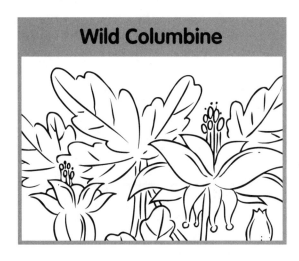

Wild Columbine

In bloom:

from _____ to _____

Height:

_____

Preferred soil:

_____

Amount of sunlight:

_____

Black-eyed Susan

In bloom:

_____

Height:

_____

Preferred soil:

_____

Amount of sunlight:

_____

2. Write two ways in which planting native plants is good for the environment.

_____

_____

_____

_____

ISBN: 978-1-897457-75-7

Experiment

Introduction

Pollution from factories mixes with water in the air. When the water falls as rain, it is more acidic than pure rainwater. This is called acid rain. Does acid rain affect plants?

Hypothesis

Check one.

Ⓐ **Acidic water, like acid rain, affects the leaf of a plant.**

Ⓑ **Acidic water, like acid rain, does not affect the leaf of a plant.**

Steps

1. Fill one spray bottle with water.

2. Fill the other one with a mixture of half vinegar and half water.

Materials

- *2 leaves on a plant that you are allowed to test*
- *2 spray bottles*
- *vinegar*
- *water*

Vinegar is an acid. We can use it to see if acidic water affects the leaf of a plant.

ISBN: 978-1-897457-75-7

3. Spray one leaf with the water and the other with the vinegar mixture.

4. Repeat the experiment every day until there is a change. Stop spraying once you see a change to protect the plant!

water

water + vinegar

Result

Fill in the table for as many days as needed. Check the correct boxes.

	Day	1	2	3	4	5	6
Water	change						
	no change						
Acidic Water	change						
	no change						

Did the acidic water affect the plant? _____

Conclusion

The hypothesis was: _____

_____

My experiment _____ the
hypothesis.   supported/did not support

Try to complete this review in **30 minutes**.

30 minutes

This review consists of five sections, from A to E. The marks for each question are shown in parentheses. The circle at the bottom right corner is for the marks you get in each section. An overall record is on the last page of the review.

A. Write T for true and F for false.

1. Both animals and plants need water. **(2)** _____

2. Plants that depend on animals for pollination have small, dull-coloured flowers. **(2)** _____

3.  Seeds need light to germinate. **(2)**

    _____

4.  Mangrove and coconut seeds are dispersed by water. **(2)**

    _____

8

ISBN: 978-1-897457-75-7

B. Do the matching.

1. 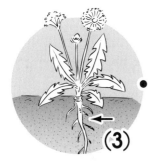 **(3)** •

2. 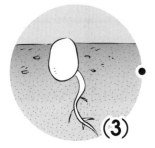 **(3)** •

3. 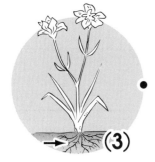 **(3)** •

4.  **(3)** •

5.  **(3)** •

- bulb: an underground stem that stores nutrients

- taproot: a single root growing downwards

- germination: process by which a seed sprouts into a seedling

- orchard: a method of growing food where fruit trees grow in rows

- fibrous roots: many small roots that spread

15

C. **Name the plant part and match it with its function. Then write the six things that plants need.**

Functions

A absorbs water and minerals and anchors the plant in soil

B moves nutrients up and down the plant; provides structural support

C uses sunlight to make food; "breathes" for the plant

D makes seeds to produce new plants

A Plant

Things Plants Need:

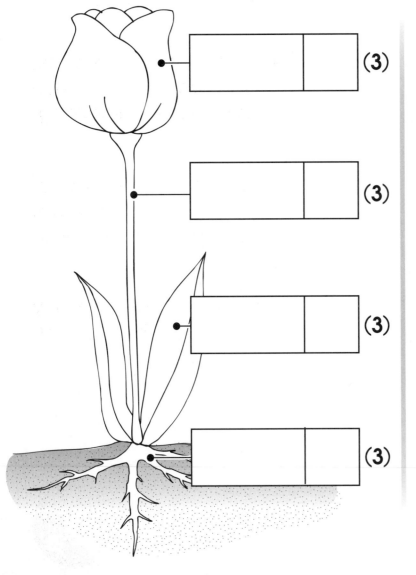

(3)

(3)

(3)

(3)

• _____ (2)

• _____ (2)

• _____ (2)

• _____ (2)

• _____ (2)

• _____ (2)

24

ISBN: 978-1-897457-75-7

D. Name each flower part and write its function. Then write about the three characteristics of flowers pollinated by animals.

1.

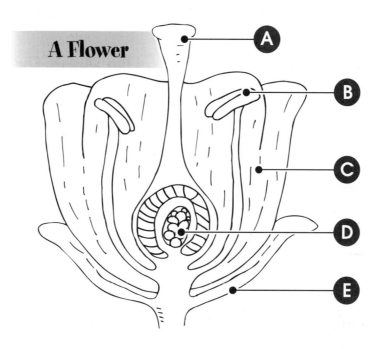

A Flower

Name

Function

A _____ **(2)**   _____ **(2)**

B _____ **(2)**   _____ **(2)**

C _____ **(2)**   _____ **(2)**

D _____ **(2)**   _____ **(2)**

E _____ **(2)**   _____ **(2)**

2. Characteristics of a flower pollinated by animals:

• _____ **(3)**

• _____ **(3)**

• _____ **(3)**

ISBN: 978-1-897457-75-7

E. Answer the questions.

1. Name two important ways that both humans and animals use plants and give a human and animal example for each. **(8)**

Use Plants for

Humans: _____

Animals: _____

Use Plants for

Humans: _____

Animals: _____

2. Briefly describe the life cycle of a cherry tree. **(8)**

_____

_____

_____

_____

_____

_____

_____

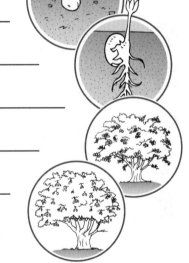

3. Describe a human activity that threatens plants and explain its impact. **(8)**

_____

_____

_____

24

ISBN: 978-1-897457-75-7

My Record

Section A		8
Section B		15
Section C		24
Section D		29
Section E		24

Total

100

80-100

Great work! You really understand your science stuff! Research your favourite science topics at the library or on the Internet to find out more about the topics related to this section. Keep challenging yourself to learn more!

60-79

Good work! You understand some basic concepts, but try reading through the units again to see whether you can master the material! Go over the questions that you had trouble with to make sure you know the correct answers.

below 60

You can do much better! Try reading over the units again. Ask your parents or teachers any questions you might have. Once you feel confident that you know the material, try the review again. Science is exciting, so don't give up!

The Botanist

Botany is the study of how plants live and grow. It is one of the world's oldest sciences, as people have been identifying edible, medicinal, and poisonous plants for thousands of years. Today, botanists study ways to produce food and medicines from plants. They also study plants in order to understand life processes and changes in the environment.

Theophrastus was a botanist who lived in Greece over two thousand years ago. He wrote two sets of books called *Enquiry into Plants* and *On the Causes of Plants*. The first set classified plants in many different ways, such as where they were found, how they reproduced, and how people could use them; the second was about farming, and how plants grow. Much of what he wrote is no longer accurate for botanists today, but his writing helped create the field of botany, and many call him the "father of botany".

ISBN: 978-1-897457-75-7

Cool Science Facts

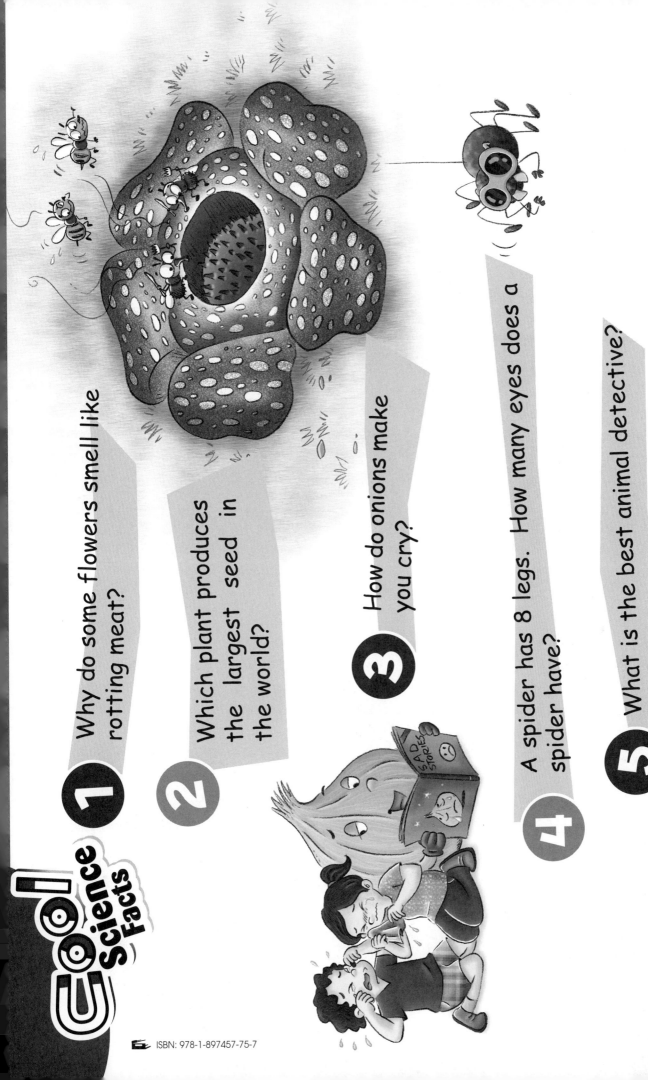

1 Why do some flowers smell like rotting meat?

2 Which plant produces the largest seed in the world?

3 How do onions make you cry?

4 A spider has 8 legs. How many eyes does a spider have?

5 What is the best animal detective?

Find the answers on the next page.

ISBN: 978-1-897457-75-7

Cool Science Facts

1

Some flowers, like the Rafflesia and the Titan Arum, smell like rotting meat because they need to attract insects such as flies and carrion beetles to transport their pollen from flower to flower.

2

The Coco de Mer produces the largest seed in the world. Its seed is often referred to as the double coconut. It can weigh up to 30 kilograms. Despite its weight, a germinated seed can float.

ISBN: 978-1-897457-75-7

5 Dogs are great detectives because of their strong sense of smell. However, one breed of dog has an ultrasensitive set of scent membranes that give it the sharpest sense of smell of all breeds. It is the bloodhound, and it is often used as a police dog, tracking missing people by following their scent trail, however faint or old the trail may be.

I follow a person's scent trail by first smelling something that has the person's scent on it, like a dress.

3 When you cut onions, they release a gas that irritates your eyes. Your eyes produce tears involuntarily to wash the gas away.

4 Many spiders have 8 eyes and some have 6, 4, or 2 eyes. Some spiders have better vision than others. Hunting spiders have good eyesight at short distance and web-building spiders have poor eyesight.

ISBN: 978-1-897457-75-7

ISBN: 978-1-897457-75-7

Section 2

Understanding Structures and Mechanisms

ISBN: 978-1-897457-75-7

1 Structures

Structures are all around us. In this unit, you will learn that both humans and animals build structures with specific functions, and that structures have many forms. The function of a structure cannot be identified by looking at its form.

After completing this unit, you will

- understand that a structure has a size, shape, and purpose.

- know that structures can be human-made or animal-made.

We are similar structures.

vocabulary

function: the purpose for which an object exists

form: the shape of a thing

support: hold or hold up

web

form: small; like a net
function: to catch prey

ISBN: 978-1-897457-75-7

Extension

A structure has different parts that are put together for a purpose. We make structures for living in, moving on, and supporting things. We put pieces of wood together to make a house so that we can have a place to live. Therefore, houses are structures.

Find the listed items in your house. Check the ones that are structures and write their functions.

Structures

☑ cup; <u>holds liquid</u>

◯ egg carton; _____

◯ newspaper; _____

◯ table; _____

A. **Every structure has a size, shape, and function. Draw lines to show which part of the lighthouse is being described.**

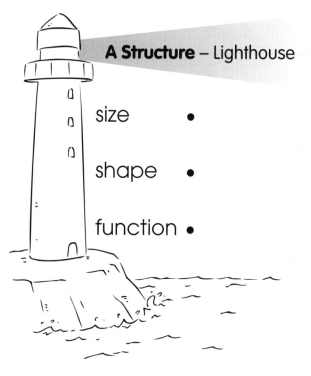

A Structure – Lighthouse

size •

shape •

function •

• The tower is 150 m tall.

• It shines a bright light to warn or guide ships at night.

• It is a cylinder with a pointed top.

ISBN: 978-1-897457-75-7

B. Match the structures with their purposes. Then circle or write the words to describe the structures.

| fence | tracks | house | water tower |

1. _____

size: **long / short**

shape: **rectangular / pointy / round**

function: to keep you in or out of a designated area

2. _____

size: **big / small**

shape: like a **ball / box**

function: to provide shelter for humans

3. _____

size: _____

shape: _____

function: to hold water and create water pressure

4. _____

size: _____

shape: _____

function: to support rail-guided transportation

ISBN: 978-1-897457-75-7

C. Identify each group of structures as "human-made" or "animal-made". Then pair up the structures that have similar functions and write about their functions.

1. _____

2. _____

spiderweb   anthill

beaver dam

mole burrow

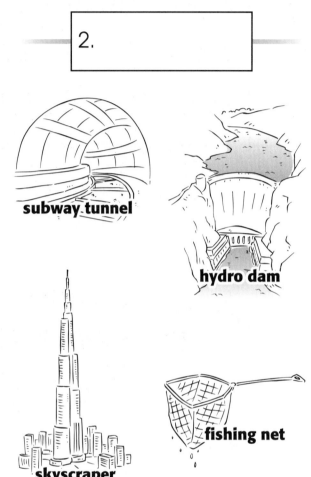

subway tunnel

hydro dam

skyscraper   fishing net

3.

Similar Structures   **Function**

• _____ and _____ : _____

• _____ and _____ : _____

• _____ and _____ : _____

• _____ and _____ : _____

ISBN: 978-1-897457-75-7

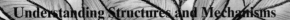

D. Read the passage. Then answer the questions.

An Amazzzzzing
Natural Structure:
the Honeycomb

A honeycomb is a natural, animal-made structure built by bees inside their nests. It is made of a wax that some bees can make in their bodies and is formed into hexagonal cells. These hexagonal cells house larvae (baby bees) and are used to store honey and pollen.

Honeycombs are remarkable structures largely because of their hexagonal cells. All cells have an almost identical shape, even if many different bees worked to make the honeycomb. Even more amazingly, the hexagonal shape ensures that the least amount of material is used to create the largest amount of storage. This is good because bees must consume a lot of honey to produce just a small amount of wax.

ISBN: 978-1-897457-75-7

1. Draw to complete the honeycomb. Then complete the description.

Honeycomb

- Structure: _____ (built by: _____)

human-made/animal-made

- Shape: _____ cells

- Material: _____

- Function: _____

2. What advantages does the honeycomb cells' hexagonal shape provide for bees?

_____

_____

_____

3. What do bees need to produce wax?

_____

ISBN: 978-1-897457-75-7

2 Forces Acting on Structures

Structures respond differently when force is applied to them. Some structures, like a wagon, are built to move. Others are built to resist force, like a table. In this unit, you will learn the effects of force on different structures.

After completing this unit, you will

- know the effect a push or pull has on a structure.

- understand that a force can move a structure, or change its shape or direction.

Mom, we shouldn't get this table. A good table should neither move nor change shape this easily.

50% OFF
ON SALE

Vocabulary

**sponge
(under compression)**

push: move something away

pull: move something closer

compression: a force that presses or squeezes something together

tension: a force that acts to expand or lengthen the thing it is acting on

 ISBN: 978-1-897457-75-7

Did you know that water can put you under compression? A simple example is when you take a shower. When water squirts out from the shower head, the small streams of water create a push force. Hence, the person who is in the shower will be under compression. If you have a high pressure shower head, the effect will be even more apparent.

Next time you take a shower, pay attention to the push force of water.

Don't forget to conserve water!

A. Write "push" or "pull" to show the force needed to do each job. Then check the correct circle to show what the outcome is.

1.

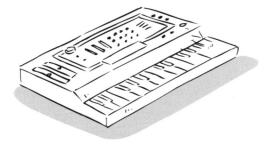

Playing the electronic keyboard:

_____ force

Ⓐ keys bend sideways

Ⓑ keys go down

Ⓒ keys go up

2.

Getting some tape:

_____ force

Ⓐ tape comes straight out

Ⓑ tape unwinds

Ⓒ tape curls around in a mess

B. Fill in the blanks with "tension" or "compression". Trace or draw arrows to show the direction of force.

The force of a push on a structure causes

1. _____ .

The force of a pull on a structure causes

2. _____ .

3.

Ⓐ

Ⓑ

Ⓒ

Ⓐ _____
Ⓑ _____
Ⓒ _____

ISBN: 978-1-897457-75-7

C. Identify the force in each situation. Then write the effect of the force.

| Force | | Effect | | |
| push | pull | moves | changes shape | changes direction |

1.  wind blowing a sidewalk sign

   Force: _____

   Effect: _____

2.  weight of the car on tires

   Force: _____

   Effect: _____

3. stretching an elastic band

   Force: _____

   Effect: _____

4. batting a baseball

   Force: _____

   Effect: _____

5. flattening dough with a rolling pin

   Force: _____

   Effect: _____

6. dragging a wagon up a slope

   Force: _____

   Effect: _____

D. Read the passage. Then answer the questions.

All instruments require a push or pull force or a combination of these forces to make music. The drum must be hit (pushed), the guitar strings strummed (pulled) and pressed (pushed), and the bagpipe squeezed (pushed). An accordionist playing the accordion is an especially interesting example of push and pull forces.

The accordion is made up of two boxes each with keys and bellows between them. The keys control which note is played, while the bellows control volume. The bellows are made from stiff materials like leather and metal for structure, and flexible materials like cloth and cardboard so that the accordionist can easily squeeze them (compression) and pull them apart (tension) to create sound. The harder the accordionist squeezes the bellows, the louder the accordion's sound is. Hence, compression and tension of the bellows control an accordion's volume.

The "Force"ful Accordion

ISBN: 978-1-897457-75-7

1. Describe what force is needed to make music with each musical instrument.

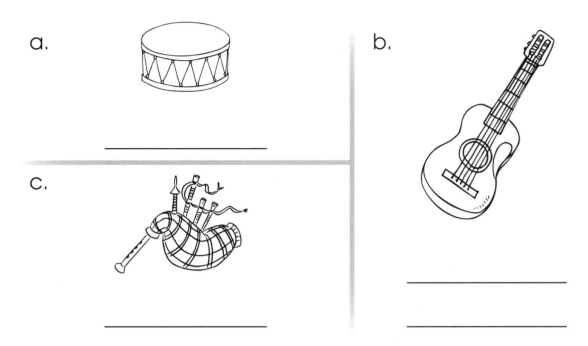

a. _____

b. _____

c. _____

2. Name the parts and functions of an accordion. Then complete the descriptions.

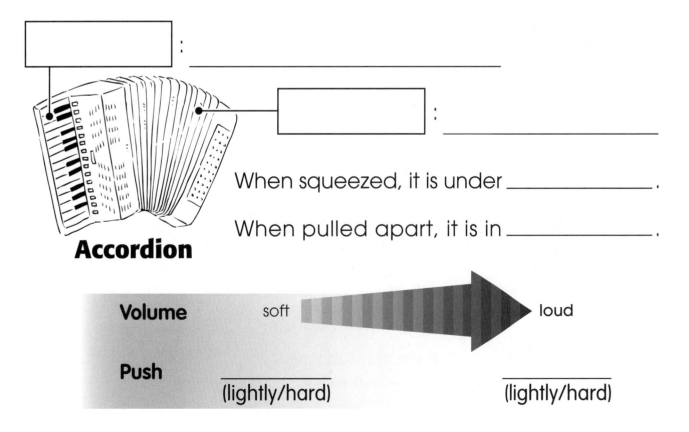

Accordion

_____ : _____

_____ : _____

When squeezed, it is under _____ .

When pulled apart, it is in _____ .

Volume   soft   ➡   loud

Push   _____   _____
        (lightly/hard)   (lightly/hard)

3 Strength and Stability

A good structure is always strong and stable. In this unit, you will learn that strong structures resist forces without breaking or changing shape. You will also learn how we can add strength and stability to a structure.

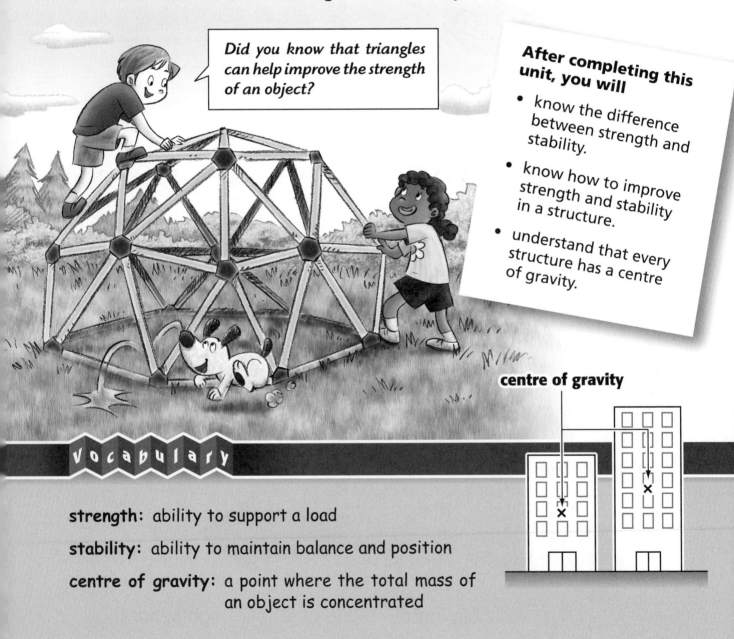

Did you know that triangles can help improve the strength of an object?

After completing this unit, you will

- know the difference between strength and stability.

- know how to improve strength and stability in a structure.

- understand that every structure has a centre of gravity.

centre of gravity

Vocabulary

strength: ability to support a load

stability: ability to maintain balance and position

centre of gravity: a point where the total mass of an object is concentrated

ISBN: 978-1-897457-75-7

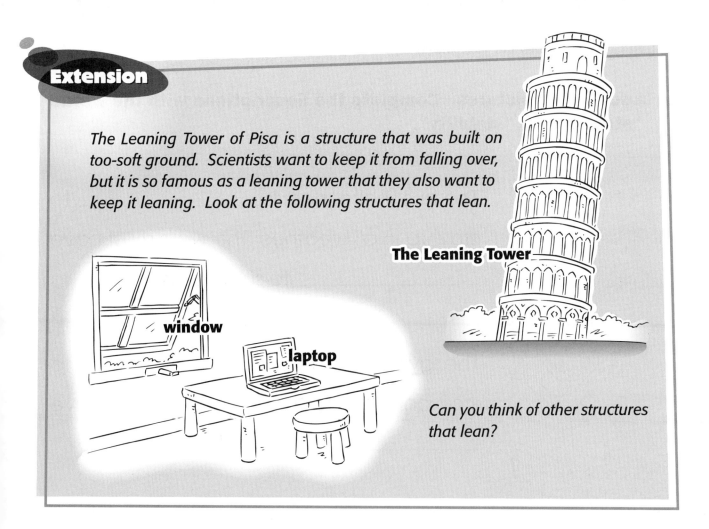

The Leaning Tower of Pisa is a structure that was built on too-soft ground. Scientists want to keep it from falling over, but it is so famous as a leaning tower that they also want to keep it leaning. Look at the following structures that lean.

The Leaning Tower

window

laptop

Can you think of other structures that lean?

A. Trace the block that should be added to each structure to make it stable.

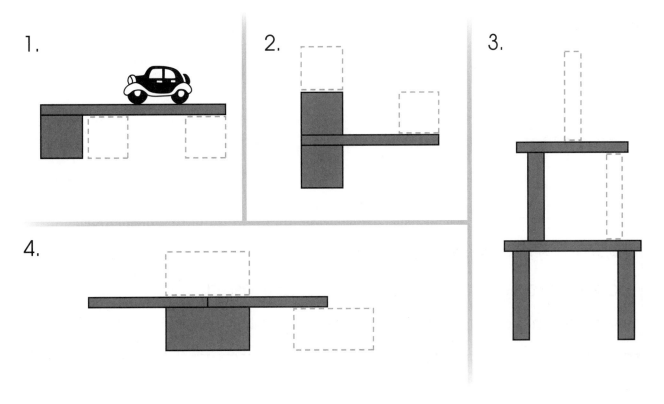

1.

2.

3.

4.

B.   Look at the pictures. Complete the descriptions with the words "strength" or "stability".

1.

The bus shelter needs _____ to stay up in all weather. The walls must have _____ to support the roof.

2.

The gymnast needs _____ to stay on the beam. The beam must have _____ to hold her up.

C.   Trace the triangles. Then fill in the blank.

A Bridge

A Hydro Tower

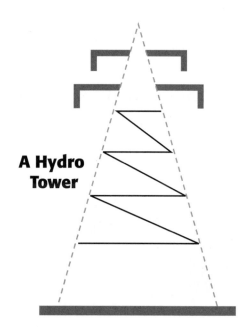

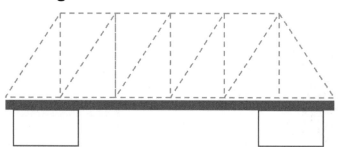

Some shapes have more stability than other shapes. _____ are used where more stability is needed.

ISBN: 978-1-897457-75-7

D. **Circle the structure with more strength and stability. Then check or give the reason.**

1.

   Gravity is always acting on structures, pulling them down from their centre of gravity. A low centre of gravity gives more stability.

   (A) longer legs
   (B) lower centre of gravity

2.

   more stable

   ✕ : centre of gravity

   (A) more stability from triangles
   (B) more flexibility from triangles

3.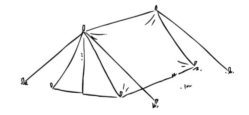

   Reason: _____

4.

   Reason: _____

E. Read the passage. Then answer the questions.

Have you ever noticed that tightrope walkers carry long, drooping poles? You might think that it would be easier to stay stable and balanced on a tightrope with your hands free, but this is not the case.

A tightrope walker carries a pole that bends downwards at its ends, lowering the tightrope walker's centre of gravity. You know that a lower centre of gravity means a more stable structure, and this is true for people, too. A tightrope walker lowers his or her centre of gravity and increases stability by carrying a pole. Some tightrope walkers even add weights to the ends of their pole to further lower their centre of gravity. This does not mean that tightrope walking is easy; it only means that it is slightly less dangerous than you may have thought.

ISBN: 978-1-897457-75-7

1. What does a tightrope walker do to gain stability? How does it work?

   _____

   _____

2. Check the correct picture to show which pole a tightrope walker uses to increase stability.

3. Sam is a tightrope walker, and he has a long, drooping pole. If he wants to increase his stability, what can he do? Make a suggestion and illustrate it.

   Suggestion:

   _____

ISBN: 978-1-897457-75-7

Introduction

A structure is often built with its base wider than its top to increase stability and strength. Take a look at this structure.

Hypothesis

Check one.

Ⓐ Of two similar structures, the one with a wider base has more stability.

Ⓑ Two similar structures have the same stability, even if one has a wider base than the other.

Steps

1. Crumple up both pieces of paper and put one piece into each cup.

2. Put the cups side by side on a table.

3. Turn one of them upside down.

Materials

- *2 identical paper or foam cups*
- *2 pieces of paper*

ISBN: 978-1-897457-75-7

4. Blow a light stream of air at each cup. Try to make the strength of the air stream the same for each cup.

5. Try a stronger stream of air.

6. Flick the cups.

7. Record your result.

Result

Record the result. (✔: stays upright; ✘: falls over)

	light air stream	strong air stream	flick
wider top			
wider base			

Conclusion

The hypothesis was: _____

_____

My experiment _____ the hypothesis.
supported/did not support

4 Structures and Materials

Structures are made from materials that suit the structures' purposes. In this unit, you will examine the properties of materials and how they suit different structures. You will also see that there are various ways to improve a structure's strength and stability.

After completing this unit, you will

- learn that materials have different properties.

- know that a structure's purpose will determine its material.

- know how to make materials stronger.

The wolf can't break in this time because brick is a strong and durable material.

wool sweater

material: wool
properties: warm, soft, light

Vocabulary

material: anything used to make a structure

property: the quality of an object

durable: long-lasting

ISBN: 978-1-897457-75-7

The materials we use to build a structure depend on the structure's purpose. However, people have to make do with what is available to them. People living in northern Canada, Greenland, and Alaska build temporary shelters with snow – an abundant material in those areas.

The dome-shaped shelters made from blocks of snow are called igloos. Even though snow blocks are a fragile building material, the dome shape gives the structure its strength. An igloo is so strong that it can provide shelter for an entire family.

A. Fill in the blanks with the given words and circle the correct answers.

flexible   durable
strong

Properties of Materials

1. A material that lasts a long time is _____ .

   Brick / Grass is a durable material.

2. A material that can bend without damage and then return to its original shape is

   _____ .

   Glass / Plastic is a flexible material.

   a flexible straw

3. A material that withstands forces being applied to it without bending or breaking is _____ .

   Paper / Steel is a strong material.

B. Read what each person says. Check the best material for the structure's purpose. Then write two properties of that material.

1.

I need a shelter for camping. It should be light and not bulky because I must carry it myself.

Material:

Ⓐ ripstop nylon

Ⓑ wood

Ⓒ concrete

Its Properties:

_____

_____

_____

2.

My sports team will practise and play games in this gym. What material should be used for the floor?

Material:

Ⓐ concrete

Ⓑ carpet

Ⓒ rubber

Its Properties:

_____

_____

_____

3.

This castle has been around for centuries! What did people use to build it?

Material:

Ⓐ rock

Ⓑ wood

Ⓒ cloth

Its Properties:

_____

_____

_____

   ISBN: 978-1-897457-75-7

C. Write the construction technique that can be applied to each material to give it more strength or stability. Then state the improvement.

Material: sheet of wood

A

Material: string

B

rope swing

Material: piece of paper

C

Tobey Winter

Material: rock

D

Construction Technique   Improved on

A by _____   _____

B by _____   _____

C by _____   _____

D by _____   _____

D. Read the passage. Then name the shelters and complete the descriptions.

Shelters in North America: Not Just Wood and Brick

During the winter, the Inuit people of the Arctic traditionally lived in dome-shaped shelters called igloos, which they built from blocks of snow. Snow is an ideal material both because it is abundant and because it traps heat. Even when it was -40°C outside, it could be as warm as 16°C inside an igloo.

Aboriginal peoples of the Canadian prairies traditionally lived in tipis: tent-like structures made from animal skins. Animal skins were durable, waterproof, and because the people were hunters, abundant. A tipi could be quickly packed up, moved, and set up again when the people moved to hunt animals.

The Pueblo people of the southwestern United States built their houses from mud bricks. These houses were called adobe houses, and they are still built today. In the southwestern United States, it is very hot, and mud bricks keep the air inside the houses cool.

   ISBN: 978-1-897457-75-7

1.

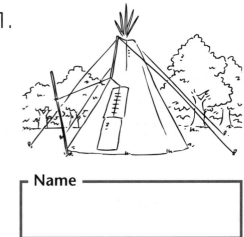

┌─ **Name** ─────────────┐
│   │
│   │
└────────────────────────┘

Built by: _____

Location: _____

Material: _____

Advantages of this Material:

_____

_____

_____

2.

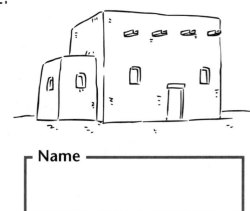

┌─ **Name** ─────────────┐
│   │
│   │
└────────────────────────┘

Built by: _____

Location: _____

Material: _____

Advantages of this Material:

_____

_____

_____

3.

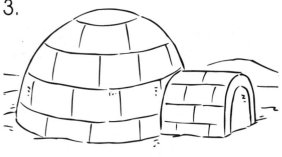

┌─ **Name** ─────────────┐
│   │
│   │
└────────────────────────┘

Built by: _____

Location: _____

Material: _____

Advantages of this Material:

_____

_____

ISBN: 978-1-897457-75-7

5 Bridges

Bridges are important structures. They span gaps that we could not otherwise cross. In this unit, you will examine the common types of bridges and the places where they are most suitably used.

After completing this unit, you will

- be able to identify types of bridges.

- understand that different bridges span different gaps.

- know how triangles are used to strengthen bridges.

It is nice to have this beam bridge because it allows us to cross the river easily.

Vocabulary

beam: a long, straight structure spanning a gap

arch: a curved, symmetrical structure

truss: a triangular support

cable: thick rope or wire

ISBN: 978-1-897457-75-7

Extension

Bridges are made by humans, but there are also natural bridges. Natural bridges are made by wind and water rubbing away rock over many thousands of years.

Owachomo Natural Bridge
Natural Bridges National Monument
Utah, U.S.A.

Maybe this beautiful natural structure inspired the people in the past to build bridges.

A. Check the correct answers.

Building Bridges

1. **Material**

Ⓐ stone Ⓑ wood

Ⓒ glass Ⓓ steel

Ⓔ concrete Ⓕ plastic

2. **Structure**

Ⓐ strong Ⓑ soft

Ⓒ transparent Ⓓ durable

Ⓔ stable: withstand the forces of nature (e.g. wind, earthquakes)

3. **Function**

Ⓐ make journeys across water easier

Ⓑ carry people between floors

Ⓒ span land that is too difficult to cross

Ⓓ make journeys for cars and pedestrians shorter and easier

B. Trace the lines. Then write the types of bridges and circle the correct answers.

Types of Bridges

truss   beam   arch   suspension

1.

B_____ Bridge

a horizontal **beam / cable** with two supports (one at each end)

2.

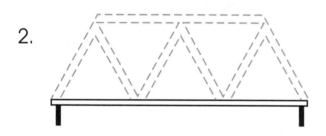

T_____ Bridge

a beam bridge strengthened by **rectangular / triangular** supports

3.

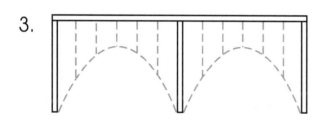

A_____ Bridge

a bridge with equal support at every point of the **truss / arch**

4.

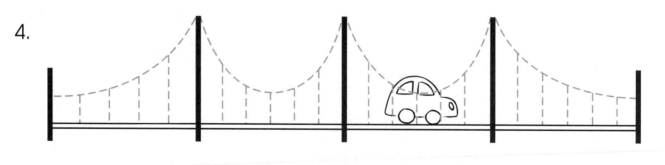

S_____ Bridge

a bridge supported by **cables / beams** attached to towers

ISBN: 978-1-897457-75-7

C. Name the type of bridge in each picture. Draw a line to match it with the best description. Then decide which type of bridge works best at each location and give a reason to support your choice.

1. _____ •

2. _____ •

3. _____ •

• good for elevated spans

• good for long spans

• spans shorter distances and is simple to construct

4. Location   Bridge (Reason)

A a deep canyon   _____ ; _____

B a shallow stream   _____ ; _____

C a lake   _____ ; _____

D. Read the passage. Name the kind of bridge shown in each picture. Then complete the descriptions.

Amazing bridges can be found all over the world. The Golden Gate Bridge is a suspension bridge completed in 1937 that connects San Francisco to northern California. It is 2737 metres long and spans San Francisco Bay. The Pont de Québec is a truss bridge in Québec City that spans the lower Saint Lawrence River. It is 987 metres long and opened in 1919 for both car and train traffic. Arch bridges have been built for thousands of years. In Spain, one such bridge, the Alcantara, is almost 2000 years old. It spans the Tagus River and is 194 metres long. Newer arch bridges include the longest arch bridge in the world, the Lupu Bridge, which was completed in 2003 in Shanghai, China. It is 3900 metres long and spans the Huangpu River.

Famous Bridges
around the World

Alcantara Bridge

ISBN: 978-1-897457-75-7

1.

Pont de Québec

- _____ bridge in _____

- span: _____

- length: _____

- opened in: _____

2.

Golden Gate Bridge

- _____ bridge

- span: _____

_____

- connects: _____

_____

- length: _____

- completed in: _____

3.

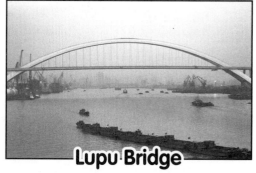

Lupu Bridge

- _____ bridge in

_____

- span: _____

- length: _____

- completed in: _____

6 Structures and Us

How do structures impact our lives? How do they impact our environment? In this unit, you will see how natural and human-made structures affect us both positively and negatively.

After completing this unit, you will

- understand that our use of materials can affect the environment.

- know that strong and stable structures affect society and the environment.

These strong and stable structures provide us with a historical record of the culture of ancient Egypt.

Vocabulary

environment: our natural surroundings

society: people in a community

positive: good

negative: bad

society

ISBN: 978-1-897457-75-7

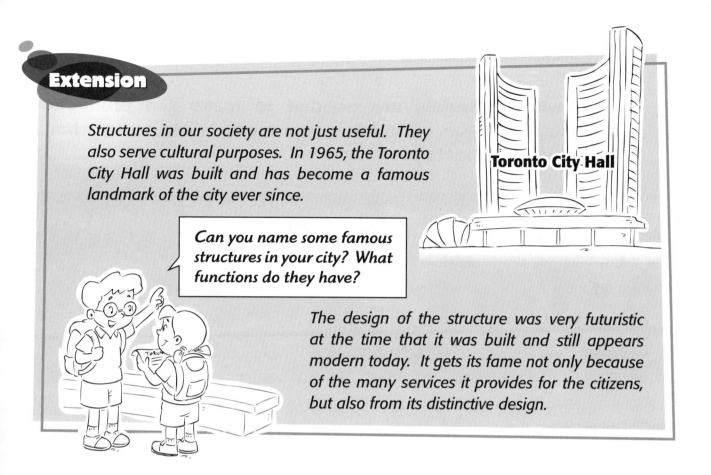

Extension

Structures in our society are not just useful. They also serve cultural purposes. In 1965, the Toronto City Hall was built and has become a famous landmark of the city ever since.

Toronto City Hall

Can you name some famous structures in your city? What functions do they have?

The design of the structure was very futuristic at the time that it was built and still appears modern today. It gets its fame not only because of the many services it provides for the citizens, but also from its distinctive design.

A. Circle the correct words to show each structure's impact. Then decide whether it is positive or negative.

1. Building New Homes

   a. **destruction / construction** of animal habitat

   _____

   b. **more / less** space for people to live in

   _____

2. Building a Hydroelectric Dam

   a. **speeding up / disrupting** the migration of fish

   _____

   b. **cutting / providing** electricity

   _____

ISBN: 978-1-897457-75-7

B. Decide what materials are needed to make the products and write where the materials come from. Then write what environmental impacts they have.

Materials	Where the Materials Come from	Environmental Impacts
• gold • plastic • wood	• forest • mining • factory	• air polluted • trees cut down • topsoil removed

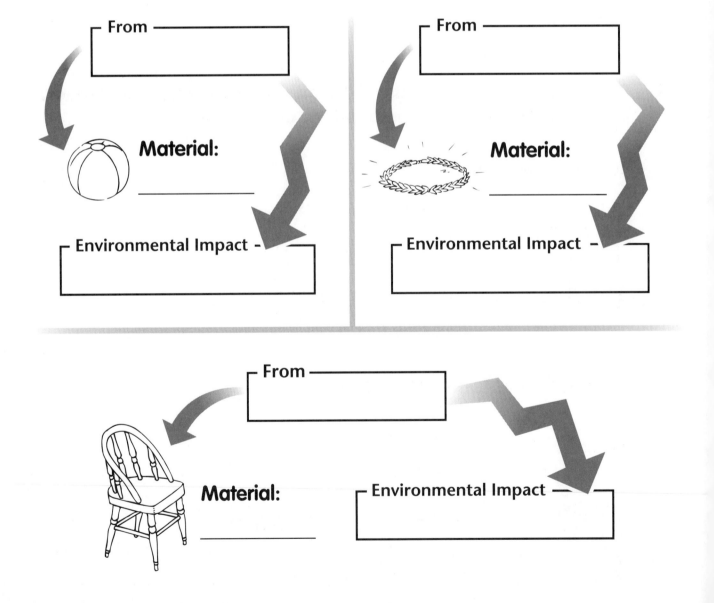

From _____

Material: _____

Environmental Impact _____

From _____

Material: _____

Environmental Impact _____

From _____

Material: _____

Environmental Impact _____

ISBN: 978-1-897457-75-7

C. **Strong and stable structures have positive and negative impacts on our society. Read about each structure and write its impact.**

1. Bridges are made with materials strong enough to carry traffic safely and they are designed to be steady even in strong winds.

   positive impact

    _____

   _____

2. Plastic ware is light but strong and durable, making it very convenient. However, it does not break down easily when it is no longer needed.

   negative impact

    _____

   _____

3. Water pipes that deliver water to our homes are made with strong materials that will not break under pressure.

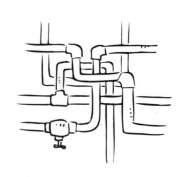

   positive impact

    _____

   _____

ISBN: 978-1-897457-75-7

The Great Wall of China

D. Read the passage. Then answer the questions.

The Great Wall of China was built in sections over a long period of time by different groups of people, but its purpose remained the same: to defend China against invaders. It is 8851 km long, spanning many landscapes, and was made of materials found in those landscapes. Its durability depends on these materials. Some sections of the wall found in plains areas were made of earth packed into blocks between wooden planks; these sections have been damaged by attacks and natural forces such as strong wind and heavy rain. Sections in the mountains were made of stone; these sections are stronger, but have still been destroyed by natural forces and by humans. Newer sections were made of brick, which was in turn made from materials found in the area. Brick is a very durable material and is most often what the best preserved sections were made of.

ISBN: 978-1-897457-75-7

1. Trace the dotted lines red to show the Great Wall of China. Then write the information.

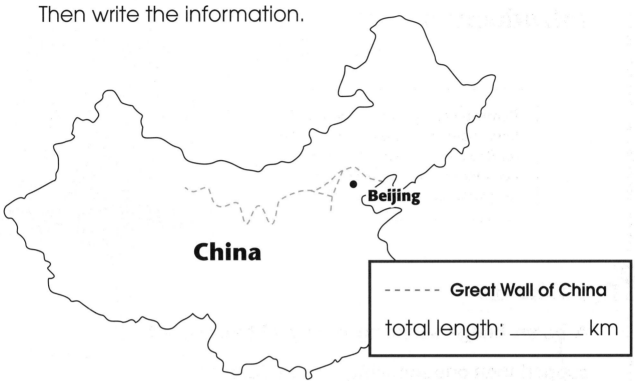

China

Beijing

----- Great Wall of China

total length: _____ km

2. What was the purpose of building the Great Wall?

    _____

3. What materials were used to build the Great Wall?

    _____

4. Why did people use the materials found in the landscape to build the Great Wall?

    _____

5. Which material is found most often in the best-preserved section of the Great Wall? Why?

    _____

6. What caused damage to the Great Wall?

    _____

Introduction

Before building a bridge, we need to know how much support is needed for it to be safe. Will a beam bridge need more or less support to span a long distance than a short distance?

?Hypothesis

A beam bridge spanning a long distance needs _____

more/less

support than one spanning a short distance.

Steps

1. From the front cover of the cereal box, cut out two beams with the dimensions of 30 cm by 6 cm and 20 cm by 6 cm.

2. Place the cups on a table to make a short span.

3. Place the short beam across the gap between the cups. Move the cups to adjust the distance if necessary.

Materials

- *a cereal box*
- *2 identical cups*
- *pennies*
- *scissors*

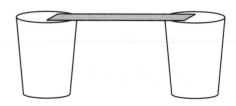

ISBN: 978-1-897457-75-7

4. Place the pennies in the middle of the beam one by one until it collapses.

5. Record the number of pennies the beam held.

6. Repeat steps 3 to 5 with a wider gap and the long beam.

Result

- **a short-span beam**

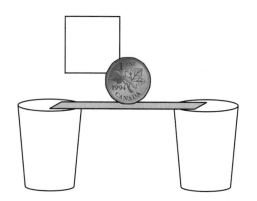

- **a long-span beam**

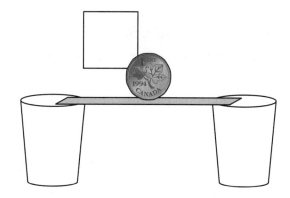

Conclusion

The hypothesis was: _____

_____

My experiment _____ the
hypothesis.   supported/did not support

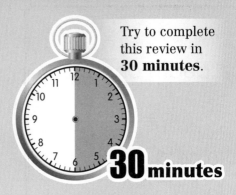

Try to complete this review in **30 minutes**.

30minutes

This review consists of five sections, from A to E. The marks for each question are shown in parentheses. The circle at the bottom right corner is for the marks you get in each section. An overall record is on the last page of the review.

A. Write T for true and F for false.

1. A structure's strength is its ability to stay balanced. (**2**) _____

2. Truss bridges are beam bridges strengthened by rectangular trusses. (**2**) _____

3.  A beaver dam is a human-made structure that is used to control water flow. (**2**)

_____

4.  Clapping one's hands causes compression on one's palms. (**2**)

_____

8

ISBN: 978-1-897457-75-7

B. Do the matching.

1.

(3)

2.

(3)

- a natural structure

- a suspension bridge

3.

(3)

- made of rock

- a pull force on a structure

4.

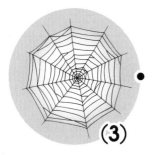

(3)

- the material used to make this object comes from forests

5.

(3)

15

ISBN: 978-1-897457-75-7

C. Name the bridges. Then answer the questions.

1. a.

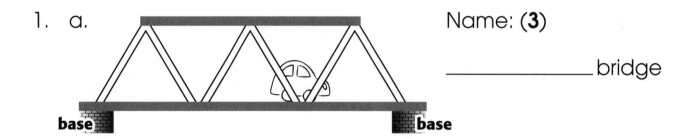

Name: **(3)**

_____ bridge

  b. What construction technique is used to strengthen this bridge? **(4)**

  _____

  c. Are the bases of the bridge under compression or in tension? **(4)**

  _____

2. a.

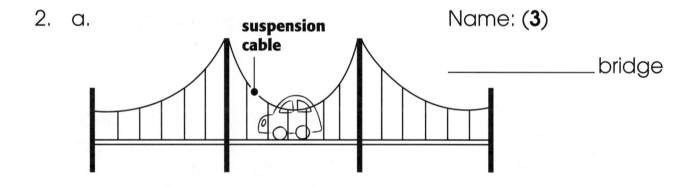

Name: **(3)**

_____ bridge

  b. What are attached to the towers to support the bridge? **(4)**

  _____

  c. When a car crosses the bridge, will the suspension cables be under compression or in tension? **(4)**

  _____

22

ISBN: 978-1-897457-75-7

D. Answer the questions about an egg carton.

Materials: (3)

1. cotton / cardboard / metal

Properties of the Material: (5)

2. _____

_____

Environmental Impact: (4)

4. _____

_____

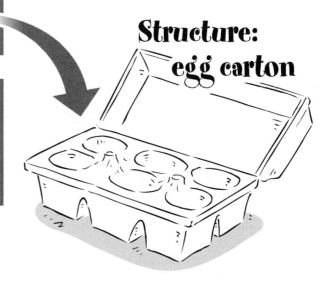

Structure: egg carton

Construction Technique Used to Increase Strength: **(3)**

3. _____

5. Function of the Structure: **(4)**

_____

6. Name and describe an animal-made structure that has the same function as an egg carton.

Name: _____ **(4)**

Size and Shape: _____ **(6)**

E. Check the correct answers and give your own example. Then answer the questions.

1. Examples of water producing a push force: **(12)**

    (A) water shooting out from a water gun

    (B) raining

    (C) drinking water

    (D) water spraying out from a spray bottle

    (✔) _____

2. Which force is associated with water being removed from a sponge? **(3)**

    tension / compression

3. What will happen to the sponge when it is under this applied force? **(3)**

    moves / changes shape / changes direction

4. What is the source of the force that keeps the ball floating? **(4)**

    _____

5. Is it a pulling or pushing force? **(4)**

    _____

26

ISBN: 978-1-897457-75-7

My Record

Section A	8
Section B	15
Section C	22
Section D	29
Section E	26

Total

100

80-100

Great work! You really understand your science stuff! Research your favourite science topics at the library or on the Internet to find out more about the topics related to this section. Keep challenging yourself to learn more!

60-79

Good work! You understand some basic concepts, but try reading through the units again to see whether you can master the material! Go over the questions that you had trouble with to make sure you know the correct answers.

below 60

You can do much better! Try reading over the units again. Ask your parents or teachers any questions you might have. Once you feel confident that you know the material, try the review again. Science is exciting, so don't give up!

The Structural Engineer

Human-built structures must be strong and stable, and structural engineers make sure that they are. These engineers design structures so that they are safe and comfortable to use and be around. Structural engineers must understand what makes a structure strong and stable, and how it supports and resists loads like water, wind, snow, and people.

One kind of structural engineer is an earthquake engineer. An earthquake engineer designs structures that can resist earthquakes, structures that are strong and stable even when the ground is unstable. Structures that can resist earthquakes help keep people safe during an earthquake because they are less likely to crumble and fall.

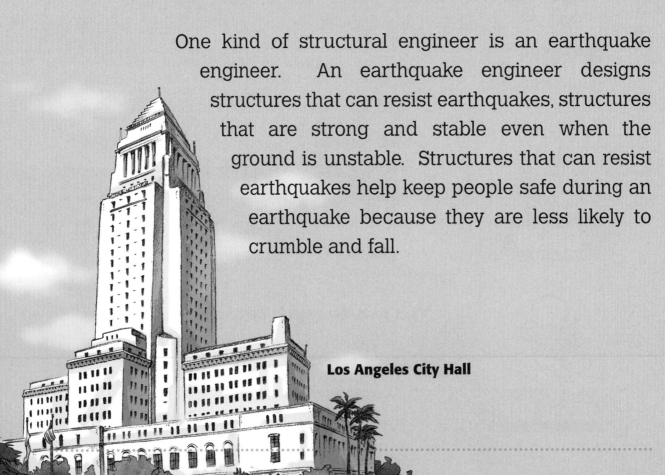

Los Angeles City Hall

ISBN: 978-1-897457-75-7

1 What simple machine turns a water tap on and off?

2 Why are manholes circular in shape?

3 What makes a couch bouncy?

4 How tall is the tallest human-made structure in the world?

5 What is the length of the longest rail tunnel in the world?

Find the answers on the next page.

ISBN: 978-1-897457-75-7

Cool Science Facts

1 A water tap uses a screw to make it work. Turning the handle turns the screw and moves the washer up and down. The washer is like a plug which fits over a hole inside the tap. When you turn the tap off, the screw pushes the washer into the hole to hold back the water from the pipe.

screw

washer
(a round rubber disc)

2 Almost all manholes are circular because the circular covers cannot fall into the holes, no matter how they are placed. The covers are always wider than the holes. If a manhole was shaped as a square, the cover could fall through the hole easily.

ISBN: 978-1-897457-75-7

4 The world's tallest human-made structure is the 828 m tall Burj Khalifa in Dubai, United Arab Emirates.

828 m

3 Springs make a couch bouncy. When you sit on a couch, you squeeze the springs. The springs return to their original length when you get off the couch. When you move up and down on a couch, the springs quickly squeeze and stretch again and again, giving you a bouncy feeling.

Seikan Tunnel

5 The longest rail tunnel in the world is 54 km long. It is called the Seikan Tunnel, and it connects Japan's two main islands.

ISBN: 978-1-897457-75-7

ISBN: 978-1-897457-75-7

Understanding Matter and Energy

ISBN: 978-1-897457-75-7

1 Force: Push or Pull

Nothing would move without a force. Forces cause trees to sway, bikes to roll, volcanoes to erupt, and planes to fly. In this unit, you will learn that anything that moves is caused by a push or a pull.

It's finally moving!

pull

push

After completing this unit, you will

• understand that a force is a push or a pull on an object.

• know that a force causes movement.

Vocabulary

force: a push or a pull causing movement or a change in movement

push: movement away from the one pushing

pull: movement towards the one pulling

pull

moving up

ISBN: 978-1-897457-75-7

Forces can be seen everywhere and in every activity that we do. It is force that causes things to move. When you kick a ball, can you see it move? Do you know that forces can also stop something that is moving? Ask your friend to roll a ball to you. Can you stop the moving ball with your hands?

A. Fill in the blanks and identify the force that causes the movement as "push" or "pull".

Force can be a 1._____

or a 2._____ .

3. _____

4. _____

ISBN: 978-1-897457-75-7

B. Determine the forces used in these activities. Write "push", "pull", or "push and pull".

1. _____

2. _____

3. _____

4. closing a fridge door _____

5. striking the keys on a keyboard _____

6. raking leaves _____

7. sawing wood _____

8. passing a basketball _____

9. brushing teeth _____

10. rowing a rowboat _____

ISBN: 978-1-897457-75-7

C. **Read the paragraph. Give an example for each situation to show how different types of forces cause movement.**

A force can cause an object to start moving, stop moving, or change direction. You can experience these forces when you go grocery shopping. You can push your cart away from you to make it move. When you apply different forces on the cart with your hands, you change the direction of the movement of the cart. If you pull the moving cart back to you, it will stop.

1. **A push** can cause things to

    • move: _____kicking a ball at rest_____

    • stop: _____

    • change direction: _____

2. **A pull** can cause things to

    • move: _____

    • stop: _____

    • change direction: _____

ISBN: 978-1-897457-75-7

2 Contact and Non-contact Forces

There are different kinds of forces. Some act through contact with the object they move; others move things without contact – they cause movement from a distance. In this unit, you will look at different kinds of forces, and identify them as contact or non-contact.

non-contact force

contact force

After completing this unit, you will

- understand that there are different kinds of forces.

- understand that a force is either a contact force or a non-contact force.

Vocabulary

gravity: force that pulls things towards Earth

buoyancy: force that keeps something floating

friction: force that slows down movement

magnetic force: push or pull force that some metal objects have

electrostatic force: force of an electrically charged object

buoyancy

ISBN: 978-1-897457-75-7

You have learned that nothing moves without a force. However, have you wondered why kites fly in the sky or wind chimes move in the air? You do not see the forces that cause these movements because they are invisible.

Place a ping-pong ball on a table. Then blow on it. Can you see that you can move the ball without touching it? There is an invisible force that pushes the ball away from you. What force is it?

moving air

A. Circle the correct word. Then check the examples that show the existence of gravity.

The **pulling / pushing** force that causes a pencil to fall to the ground is gravity.

Existence of Gravity

A) leaves falling to the ground

B) a coin rolling down a slope

C) dropping a key to the floor

D) skiing down a hill

B. Write each type of force. Then identify it as a "contact" or a "non-contact" force.

Types of Forces

magnetic   buoyancy   friction   muscular   gravity
wind   electrostatic   moving water

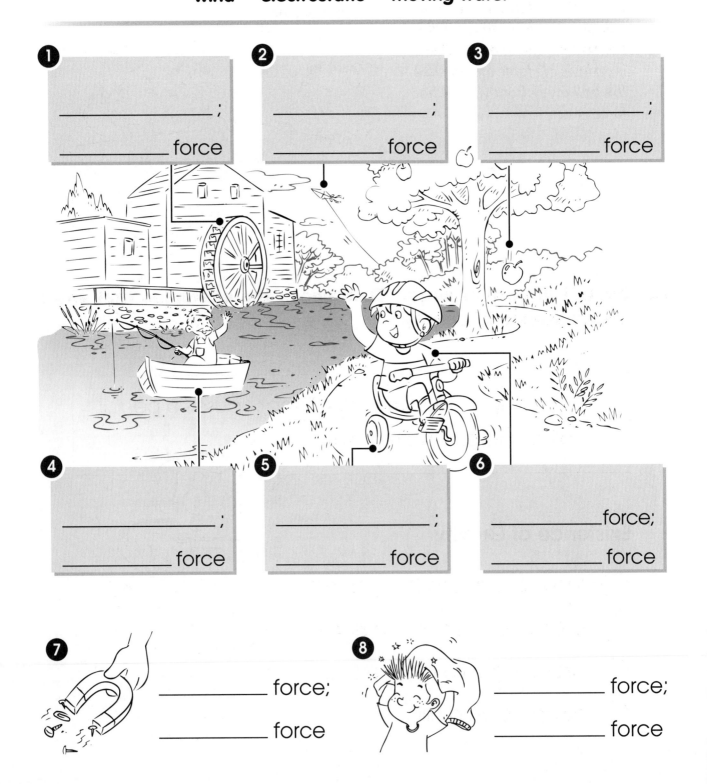

① _____ ;
_____ force

② _____ ;
_____ force

③ _____ ;
_____ force

④ _____ ;
_____ force

⑤ _____ ;
_____ force

⑥ _____ force;
_____ force

⑦ _____ force;
_____ force

⑧ _____ force;
_____ force

ISBN: 978-1-897457-75-7

C. Read the paragraphs. Label the diagrams and answer the question with the words in bold. Then give two examples.

A magnet is an object that can push or pull materials made of **iron**, **steel**, or **nickel**. A magnet is made of these same materials. Every magnet has a north pole and a **south** pole at each of its ends, which is where its force is the strongest. Like poles of magnets **repel**; unlike poles **attract**.

Magnets are very useful in many areas of our daily lives. A fridge door is a good example.

magnetic strip

1.

a magnet

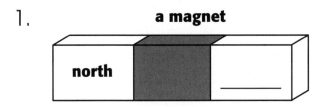

north _____

2. a. _____

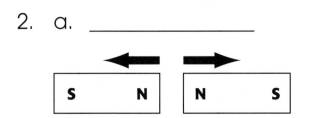

b. _____

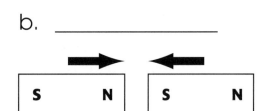

3. What is a magnet made of?

_____

4. Name two objects that make use of magnetic forces.

_____

ISBN: 978-1-897457-75-7

3 Forces and Movement

Forces cause movement. In this unit, you will see how forces cause objects to move in different ways, or not move at all if the two opposing forces are balanced.

After completing this unit, you will

- understand how different forces can cause a moving object to keep the same speed, speed up, slow down, change direction, or stop.

- know that movement is caused by unbalanced forces.

The man and his dog have been here for a while and haven't moved at all. They show balanced forces.

Vocabulary

balanced forces: equal amounts of forces on both sides

unbalanced forces: unequal amounts of forces on both sides

unbalanced forces

ISBN: 978-1-897457-75-7

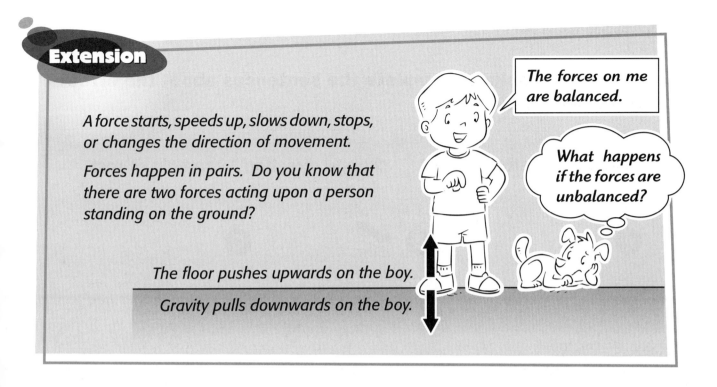

A force starts, speeds up, slows down, stops, or changes the direction of movement.

Forces happen in pairs. Do you know that there are two forces acting upon a person standing on the ground?

The floor pushes upwards on the boy.

Gravity pulls downwards on the boy.

The forces on me are balanced.

What happens if the forces are unbalanced?

A. Look at each pair of arrows. Decide whether the forces are "balanced" or "unbalanced". Then do the matching.

The bigger the arrows are, the greater the forces.

_____ forces

_____ forces

_____ forces

• moves to the left

• moves to the right

• stays at rest

B. Fill in the blanks to complete the sentences about the effects of forces on the objects.

| speed up | stop | start | change direction | remain at rest |

A The sailing yacht will _____ due to the force of wind if wind blows from another direction.

B The paper plane will _____ due to muscular force.

C The roller-coaster will _____ due to the force of gravity.

D The toy car will _____ due to balanced opposing forces.

E The soccer ball will eventually _____ due to the force of friction.

ISBN: 978-1-897457-75-7

C. Read the paragraph. Write T for true and F for false. Then draw an arrow to show balanced forces.

Balanced forces are at work on a soccer ball when it is at rest: the ball pushes on the ground and the ground pushes back. However, when a soccer player kicks the ball, his motion creates unbalanced forces, which cause the ball to move. Other forces, such as gravity and friction, act on these unbalanced forces until the ball comes to a stop, and the forces acting on it are once again balanced.

1. When a ball is at rest, it has balanced forces.

   _____

2. Unbalanced forces can cause a ball at rest to move.

   _____

3. Unbalanced forces are at work on a ball when it is in the air.

   _____

4. Draw an arrow to show the force from the ground that acts on the ball.

Balanced Forces

ISBN: 978-1-897457-75-7

Introduction

Isaac Newton's
First Law of Motion

An object at rest will stay at rest, and an object in motion will stay in motion – unless another force acts to change that.

Think of an egg as having two parts:

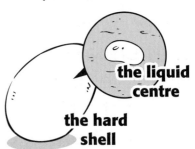

the liquid centre

the hard shell

If you spin the egg and then stop it with your fingers, you are stopping only the shell. The liquid inside will stay in motion until something also stops it. At least that is what should happen according to Newton's first law of motion.

?Hypothesis

If a raw egg is spinning, and is then stopped, the liquid centre will continue to spin.

Steps

1. Spin the cooked egg on the big plate.

Materials

- *one raw egg*
- *one hard-boiled egg*
- *a big plate*

ISBN: 978-1-897457-75-7

2. Stop the egg from spinning by putting a finger on it for a moment. Remove your finger almost as soon as you touch the egg.

3. Repeat steps 1 and 2 with the raw egg.

Result

Record your observations. What did the egg do after you stopped it with your finger?

Cooked egg: _____

_____

Raw egg: _____

_____

The raw egg will continue to spin after it is stopped because the liquid inside keeps moving. It does stop eventually because of other forces acting on it.

Conclusion

The hypothesis was: _____

_____

My experiment _____ the hypothesis.
                        supported/did not support

4 Friction

Friction occurs when two things rub together. Friction can cause problems, but it also helps us in many ways in our everyday lives. In this unit, you will take a closer look at friction and know how much friction is needed in different activities.

After completing this unit, you will

- know that friction occurs when two things rub together.

- know that friction resists movement.

- understand that different activities need different amounts of friction.

movement

friction

The less friction there is, the faster I can go.

Vocabulary

friction: a force that resists motion when two things are in contact

**friction
(two things rubbing)**

ISBN: 978-1-897457-75-7

Get a toy car and try to push it on different surfaces to see how far it can go. Make predictions. Then record your findings.

How Far It Can Go

	Prediction	Findings
carpet	far/not far	
table		
floor		

Do you know why the toy car can go farther on smooth surfaces? What force slows down the toy car?

A. Circle the correct words to complete the paragraph about friction.

...rough surface... great friction

movement

friction

Friction is a **force / job** that acts against motion. Working in the **same / opposite** direction of the force causing movement, it slows objects down or even causes them to **stop / lock** . This only happens if **contact / a pull** is made. The rougher the surface is, the **smaller / greater** the friction it has.

B. **Colour the arrows to show the motion and friction. Then write "more" or "less" to show how much friction is required in each activity.**

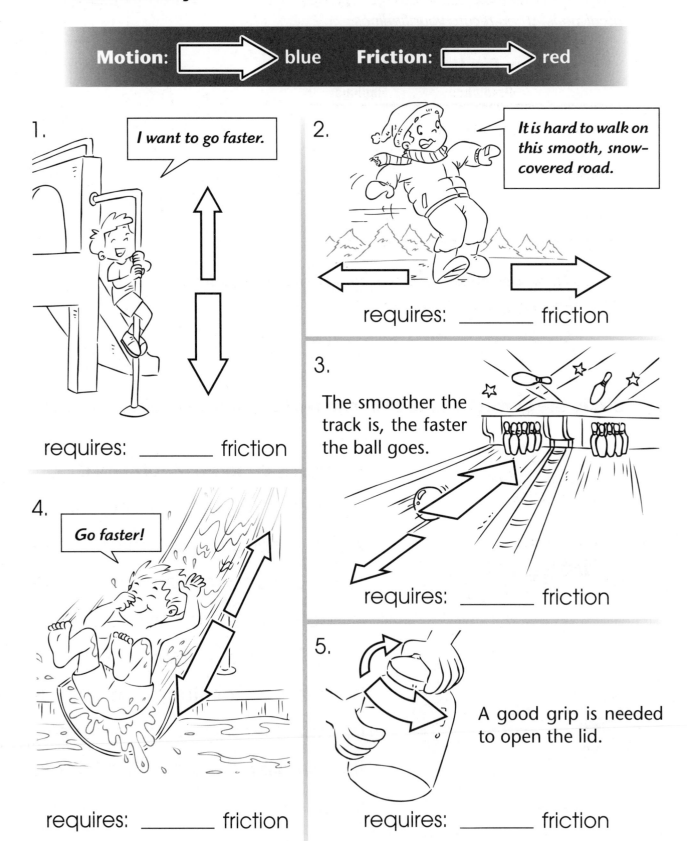

Motion: ➡ blue   Friction: ➡ red

1. *I want to go faster.*

requires: _____ friction

2. *It is hard to walk on this smooth, snow-covered road.*

requires: _____ friction

3. The smoother the track is, the faster the ball goes.

requires: _____ friction

4. *Go faster!*

requires: _____ friction

5. A good grip is needed to open the lid.

requires: _____ friction

ISBN: 978-1-897457-75-7

C. Read the paragraph. Fill in the boxes with the words in bold. Then answer the question.

Friction is very important when driving a car. Without it, a car would skid off the road. On a **dry** road, there is **a lot of** friction between car tires and the **rough** road surface. In the winter, however, when there is snow or ice on the road, there is only **a little** friction between tires and the road because the road surface is **smooth**. This is why we need winter tires. Winter tires have special grooves to increase friction in snowy or **icy** conditions.

1.

_____ , _____
surface

_____ or _____
surface

_____ friction

_____ friction

2. What tires should be used in the winter to help people drive safely? Why do they help?

_____

_____

5 Forces in Nature

There are many different kinds of forces in nature. In this unit, you will learn how the forces in nature can be helpful to us and what damage they may cause.

After completing this unit, you will

- know that forces occur in nature.
- be able to identify different forces in nature.
- understand that forces in nature can be helpful or damaging.

High winds and heavy rain warnings have been issued. Precautions must be taken to prevent and reduce damage.

Vocabulary

destructive: causing a lot of damage

extreme: at the most; severe

erosion: wearing away of the earth's surface

erosion (caused by moving water)

ISBN: 978-1-897457-75-7

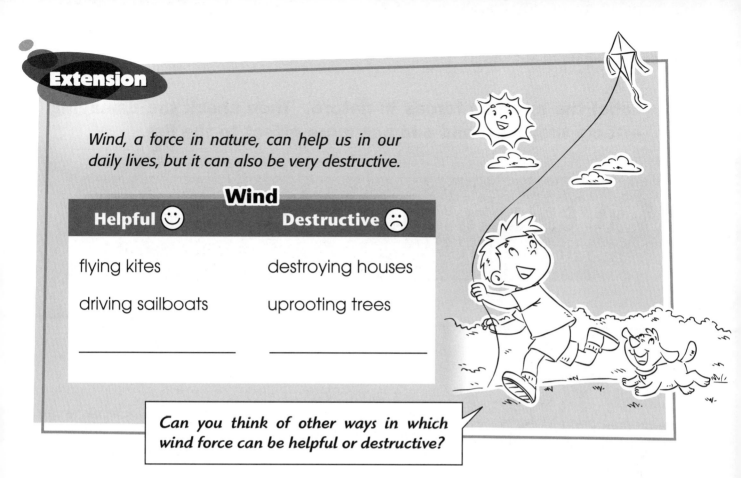

Wind, a force in nature, can help us in our daily lives, but it can also be very destructive.

Wind

Helpful 😊	Destructive ☹
flying kites	destroying houses
driving sailboats	uprooting trees
_____	_____

Can you think of other ways in which wind force can be helpful or destructive?

A. Match the forces in nature with the correct descriptions.

moving water   buoyancy
lightning   magnetism
hurricane

Forces in Nature

1. _____ : an extreme, windy condition

2. _____ : a charge in a storm caused by static electricity

3. _____ : a waterfall is an example of this force

4. _____ : the force that keeps clouds in the sky

5. _____ : the force that can be found in a rock containing iron

ISBN: 978-1-897457-75-7

B. **Label the extreme forces in nature. Then check the damaging effects they have and add one more effect to the list.**

 **in Nature**

earthquake   flood
lightning   tornado   landslide
volcanic eruption

_____   _____   _____

_____   _____   _____

**Damaging Effects
of
Extreme Forces**

◯ cause erosion

◯ destroy houses and buildings

◯ destroy natural habitats

✔ _____

ISBN: 978-1-897457-75-7

C. Read the paragraph. Then answer the questions.

Volcanic eruptions cause great damage, but they have benefits as well. The molten rock that erupts from volcanoes comes from deep below the Earth's surface. This molten rock, called magma, is rich in minerals. When a volcano erupts, these minerals come to the Earth's surface as lava and ash. Eventually, the lava cools, the ash settles, and both break down into soil that is perfect for farming. This is one of the reasons why people live close to dormant* volcanoes.

once erupted; not active now, but could erupt again

1.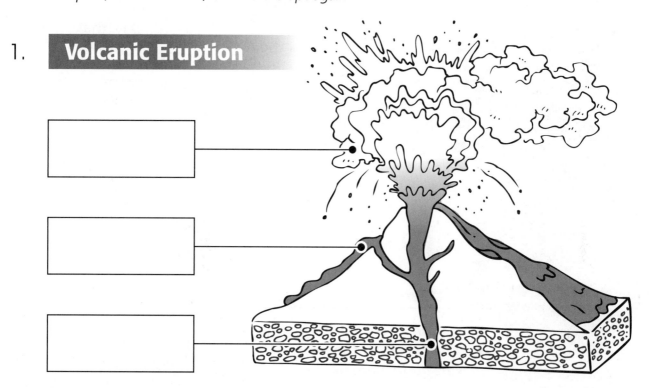

Volcanic Eruption

2. Where is magma found? What does magma contain?

_____

3. Why do people live close to dormant volcanoes?

_____

_____

ISBN: 978-1-897457-75-7

6 Forces in Our Lives

We use forces to make our lives easier. In this unit, you will understand how we use forces. You will see how people use their knowledge of forces in their jobs, and see that physics, the study of forces, is extremely useful to us.

After completing this unit, you will

- be able to identify jobs that require knowledge of forces.
- understand how we use forces in our daily lives.

Dad, can you see that the windmill converts the energy of moving air to motion?

Vocabulary

physics: the science of matter, motion, and force

turbine: a wheel-like machine driven by moving air or water

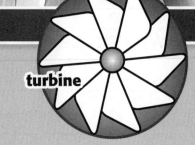
turbine

ISBN: 978-1-897457-75-7

Do you know that various forces are involved even in a simple activity like blow-drying your hair?

Forces Involved:

moving air: helps you dry your hair

muscular force: lets you hold up the hair dryer

friction: gives you a good grip of the hair dryer

gravitational force: keeps you on the floor

There are at least five forces involved in the activity of rowing a boat. Do you know what they are?

A. Match the descriptions with the correct jobs. Write the letters.

A studies forces that affect weather

B studies how forces affect the human body

C studies forces that shape the Earth

D studies how forces affect buildings

○ biomechanist

○ meteorologist

○ engineer

○ geologist

People study forces to see how they can be controlled and used. There are many jobs that require knowledge of how forces work.

B. Find the forces at work in the pictures. Write the letters.

A magnetic force   **B** muscular force   **C** friction

D gravitational force   **E** electrostatic force   **F** buoyancy

G force of moving air   **H** force of moving water

1. a.

b.
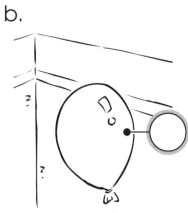

c.

2.

3.

4.

ISBN: 978-1-897457-75-7

C. Read the paragraph. Then answer the questions.

Wind farms all over Canada harness wind force to produce electricity using huge turbines that look much like giant white windmills. Some of Canada's largest wind farms have over 100 turbines and produce enough electricity to power tens of thousands of homes; some of the smallest have only four or five turbines. Many turbines stand over 80 metres tall from the ground to the highest blade, and a blade is about 45 metres in length.

1. **A Turbine**

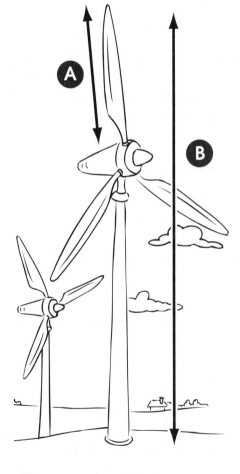

A: about _____

B: about _____

2. What are wind farms used for? How do they work?

_____

_____

_____

3. About how many wind turbines can be found in the largest wind farms in Canada?

_____

4. Scientists help the government choose a site for building a wind farm. What should they study?

Ⓐ the water power at the site

Ⓑ the wind power at the site

Ⓒ the weight of a turbine

ISBN: 978-1-897457-75-7

Introduction

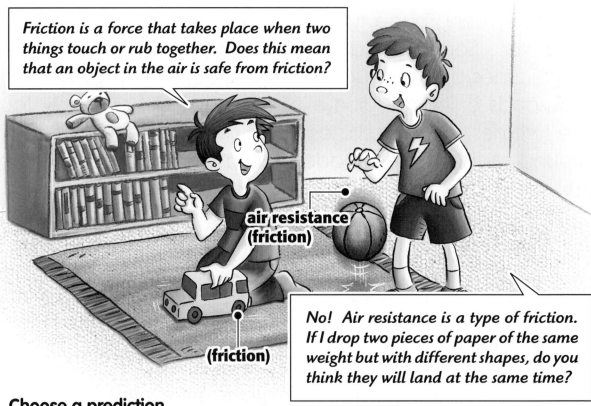

> *Friction is a force that takes place when two things touch or rub together. Does this mean that an object in the air is safe from friction?*

air resistance
(friction)

(friction)

> *No! Air resistance is a type of friction. If I drop two pieces of paper of the same weight but with different shapes, do you think they will land at the same time?*

Choose a prediction.

When you drop two pieces of paper, one crumpled and one not crumpled:

Prediction 1	They will land at the same time.
Prediction 2	The crumpled one encounters less friction, so it will land first.
Prediction 3	The non-crumpled one encounters less friction, so it will land first.

? Hypothesis

The hypothesis based on the prediction you chose:

_____

_____

Materials

- *2 pieces of paper of the same size and weight*

Steps

1. Crumple up one of the pieces of paper into a ball.

2. Hold the intact piece of paper in one hand and the crumpled paper in the other hand.

3. Let them drop to the ground.

Be sure to let go of them at exactly the same time.

Result

Which one landed first: the crumpled paper or the non-crumpled paper?

_____

Conclusion

The hypothesis was: _____

_____

My experiment _____ the hypothesis.
supported/did not support

Try to complete this review in **30 minutes**.

30 minutes

This review consists of five sections, from A to E. The marks for each question are shown in parentheses. The circle at the bottom right corner is for the marks you get in each section. An overall record is on the last page of the review.

A. Write T for true and F for false.

1. We can use a push force to cause things to move. **(2)** _____

2. If you want to stop something that is moving away from you, you have to apply a push force to it. **(2)** _____

3.

   You need friction between your hand and the lid when you open a jar. **(2)**

   _____

4.

   Buoyancy is a force that exists in water. **(2)**

   _____

8

ISBN: 978-1-897457-75-7

B. Do the matching.

1.
(3)

2.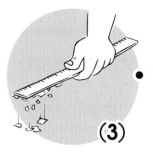
(3)

3.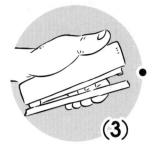
(3)

4.
(3)

5.
(3)

- needs a push force

- electrostatic force is at work

- a meteorologist studies these forces

- speeds up due to gravity

- shows balanced opposing forces

15

ISBN: 978-1-897457-75-7

C. **Draw lines to show which force makes each object move and identify each force. Then answer the questions.**

1.

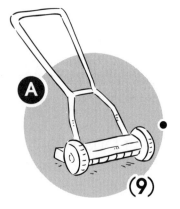

(9)

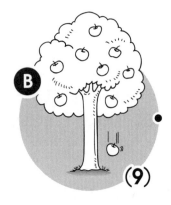

(9)

What Moves the Object:

• force of moving water

• gravitational force

• magnetic force

• muscular force

• electrostatic force

How the Force Acts on the Object:

• a **push** force

• a **pull** force

• a **contact** force

• a **non-contact** force

2. Mr. Winter is using Ⓐ to mow his lawn. He finds that there is a force that acts against his motion.

   a. Does it slow down or speed up his motion? **(3)**

   _____

   b. What force is it? **(3)**

   _____

24

ISBN: 978-1-897457-75-7

D. Look at the picture. Answer the questions.

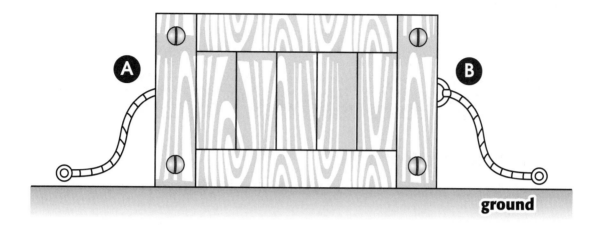

Sue pulls the box at Ⓐ to cause a movement.

1. In what direction does the box move? **(4)**

   _____

2. Which forces, balanced or unbalanced, cause the movement? **(4)**

   _____

3. If Jack pulls at Ⓑ with the same effort and at the same time as Sue, what will happen to the box? **(4)**

   _____

4. When both children pull with the same effort, which forces, balanced or unbalanced, act on the box? **(4)**

   _____

5. Are the forces acting on the box in the same or opposite directions? **(4)**

   _____

20

ISBN: 978-1-897457-75-7

E. Match the descriptions with the extreme forces in nature. Write what force is at work in each. Then write what forces are at work in our lives.

Forces at Work

gravity   moving water   moving air   friction
muscular force   buoyancy   electrostatic force

1. **Extreme Forces in Nature**

- violent wind storm

  force at work: _____ **(3)**

flood   **(3)** •

landslide **(3)** •

hurricane **(3)** •

- rapid downward sliding of a mass of soil or rock on a steep slope

  force at work: _____ **(3)**

- great flowing or overflowing of water over land

  force at work: _____ **(3)**

2. **Forces at Work in Our Lives**

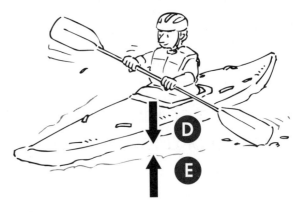

A _____ (3)

B _____ (3)

C _____ (3)

D _____ (3)

E _____ (3)

33

ISBN: 978-1-897457-75-7

My Record

Section **A**		8
Section **B**		15
Section **C**		24
Section **D**		20
Section **E**		33

Total

100

Great work! You really understand your science stuff! Research your favourite science topics at the library or on the Internet to find out more about the topics related to this section. Keep challenging yourself to learn more!

80-100

Good work! You understand some basic concepts, but try reading through the units again to see whether you can master the material! Go over the questions that you had trouble with to make sure you know the correct answers.

60-79

You can do much better! Try reading over the units again. Ask your parents or teachers any questions you might have. Once you feel confident that you know the material, try the review again. Science is exciting, so don't give up!

below 60

ISBN: 978-1-897457-75-7

The Roller Coaster Designer

If you are brave enough to ride the tallest and fastest roller coasters, you may be interested in becoming a roller coaster designer.

Roller coaster designers are engineers. They must understand gravity and inertia. Both concepts are essential to the design of "lift hill" roller coasters, which begin with a huge hill that roller coaster cars climb and descend. Once the cars are at the top of this huge hill, it is gravity that pulls them down and provides them with enough energy to move through the track. Inertia is the cars' tendency to keep moving once a force has put them in motion. Once gravity gets the cars moving, their inertia keeps them moving until they get to the end of the track. The taller a designer makes the initial hill, the faster and farther the "lift hill" roller coaster cars can go. Does this sound like a job for you?

ISBN: 978-1-897457-75-7

Cool Science Facts

1 How does an eraser work?

2 How does a train without wheels work?

3 Which animal is the strongest animal relative to its body weight?

4 Can you tell salt and sugar apart without tasting them?

5 How are diamonds and graphite closely related to each other?

Salt? Sugar?

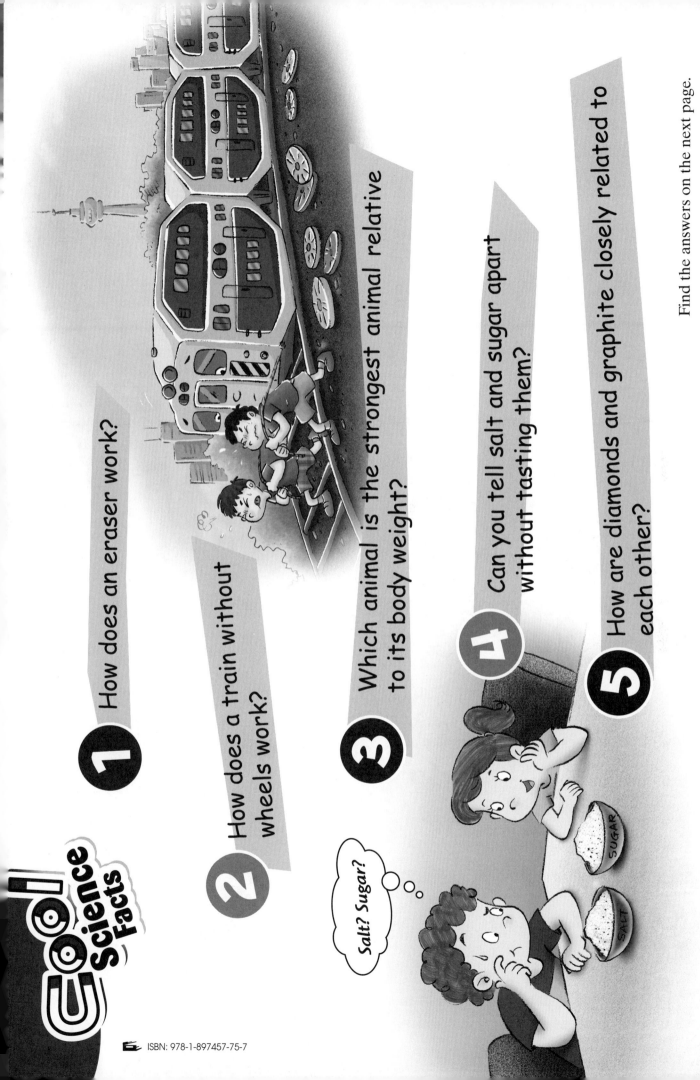

Find the answers on the next page.

ISBN: 978-1-897457-75-7

2

People use electron magnets in a train. This train has no wheels, but it has magnets. The train and the rails contain magnets that repel each other. It is this magnetic power that makes the train hover and move forward without touching the rails.

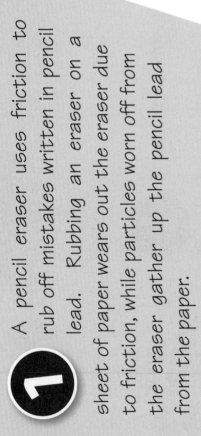

1

A pencil eraser uses friction to rub off mistakes written in pencil lead. Rubbing an eraser on a sheet of paper wears out the eraser due to friction, while particles worn off from the eraser gather up the pencil lead from the paper.

ISBN: 978-1-897457-75-7

Sugar

Salt

4 It is easy to tell salt and sugar apart with a magnifying glass. Sugar crystals are longer with slanted ends and salt crystals look like cubes.

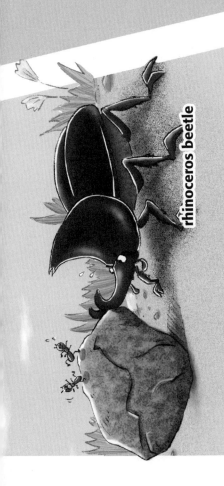

rhinoceros beetle

3 When we refer to the strongest animal, we mean how much an animal can carry relative to its own weight. An elephant can carry about 25% of its own weight, a camel about 20%, and a rhinoceros beetle about 850 times. That is why the rhinoceros beetle is the strongest animal in the world.

5 Diamonds and graphite are made of the same chemical element – carbon. The carbon atoms in graphite arrange themselves in sheets that are only loosely bonded, but in a diamond, the carbon atoms are strongly bonded in a compact form.

ISBN: 978-1-897457-75-7

ISBN: 978-1-897457-75-7

Section 4

Understanding Earth and Space Systems

ISBN: 978-1-897457-75-7

1 Soil

Soil is all around us, and it is much more than just dirt. In this unit, you will classify the four components of soil and learn where soil is found.

After completing this unit, you will

- understand that soil is made up of four components.
- know where soil is found.

decaying organic materials

air →

Let me show you the living and non-living things in soil.

rock particles

water

Vocabulary

component: part of something

particle: very small bit of matter

organic: from living or once-living things

inorganic: from non-living things

plastic: inorganic

wood: organic

ISBN: 978-1-897457-75-7

When you see colourful flowers around you, do you notice that soil, an important element for a plant's growth, also has different colours? Soil can be black, red, brown, yellow, or grey. Soil colour can tell us whether or not the soil is good for plants. In general, the darker the soil is, the more nutrient-rich it is.

Make a chart to record the colours of the soil that you find around you and think about which of those places is best for plants.

Colour of Soil

at home _____

backyard _____

park _____

farm _____

beach _____

A. Check the places where soil exists on Earth.

Ⓐ in forests

Ⓑ in backyards

Ⓒ under grass

Ⓓ under a glacier

Ⓔ in the sky

Ⓕ on a mountain ledge

Ⓖ **on an ice cap**

Ⓗ **at the silty bottom of a stream**

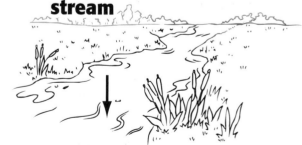

B. Read what Melissa says. Then match the pictures with the correct descriptions. Write the letters.

> *Rock particles are major components of soil. Do you know how rock breaks down into small pieces to become a part of soil?*

A Moving water breaks apart rocks.

B Plant roots crack rocks apart.

C Water seeps into cracks and expands when it freezes.

D Wind breaks apart and moves pieces of rock.

E Glaciers scrape rocks as they move down the mountainside.

Rocks ⟶ Soil

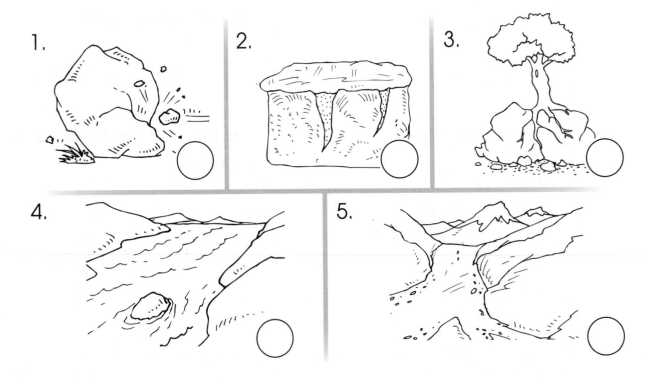

ISBN: 978-1-897457-75-7

C. Fill in the blanks to complete the paragraph. Then answer the question.

Soil's Ingredients

water   minerals   organic   earthworms   inorganic

Soil is made up of a variety of substances. These substances can be classified into four groups. They are organic materials, 1._____ materials, air, and 2._____ . 3._____ materials come from things that are living or were once living, such as 4._____ and leaves. Inorganic materials, such as 5._____ and iron, are not and never were living.

6. Sort the items. Write the letter.

   A bacteria

   B decaying leaves

   C rock particles

   D animal waste

   E air

   F water

   G twigs

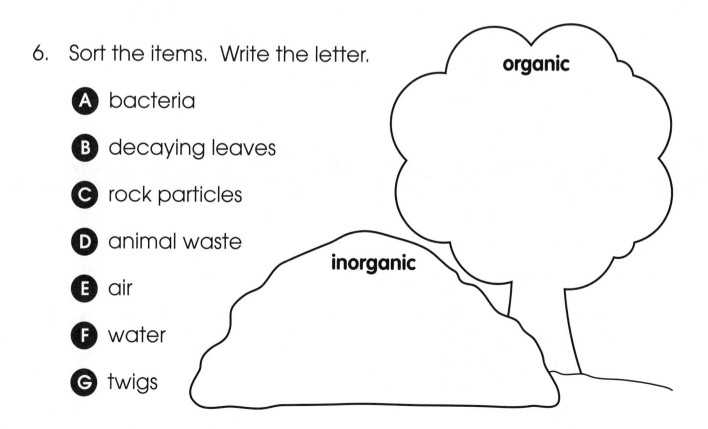

organic

inorganic

2 Kinds of Soil

Rock particle size is important when it comes to soil. In this unit, you will identify soils by rock particle size and see how these different soils interact differently with water.

After completing this unit, you will

- be able to identify and describe different types of soil.

- understand how different soils interact with water differently.

Sand is not the right soil for the flowers in our backyard, but it is just right for this "flower"!

Vocabulary

sand: soil with the largest rock particles

clay: soil with the finest rock particles

silt: soil with rock particles bigger than clay and smaller than sand

humus: organic part of soil

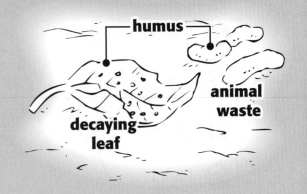

ISBN: 978-1-897457-75-7

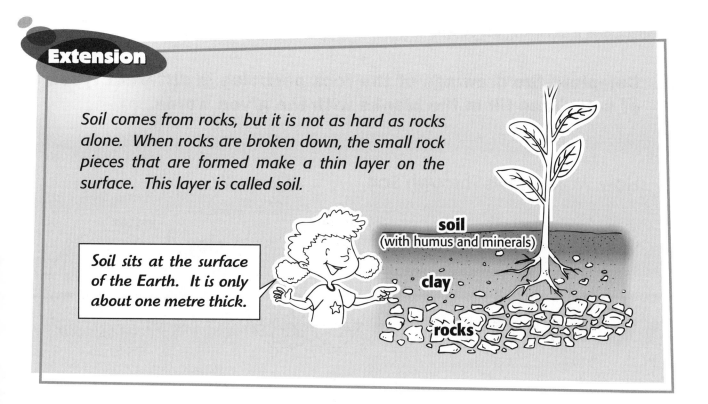

Soil comes from rocks, but it is not as hard as rocks alone. When rocks are broken down, the small rock pieces that are formed make a thin layer on the surface. This layer is called soil.

Soil sits at the surface of the Earth. It is only about one metre thick.

soil
(with humus and minerals)

clay

rocks

A. **Look at the rock particles in different types of soil. Then answer the questions.**

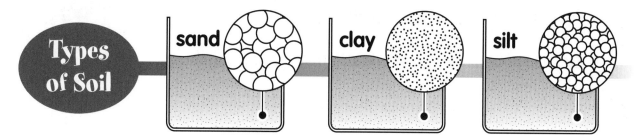

Types of Soil

sand

clay

silt

1. Which type of soil has the largest rock particles? _____

2. Which type of soil has the smallest rock particles? _____

3. Compare the size of the rock particles in different types of soil. Write two sentences to describe them.

_____

_____

ISBN: 978-1-897457-75-7

B. Complete the drawings of the rock particles in different types of soil. Then fill in the blanks with the given words.

1. **How Water Flows Through Soil**   ∗ Add the same amount of water to each soil.

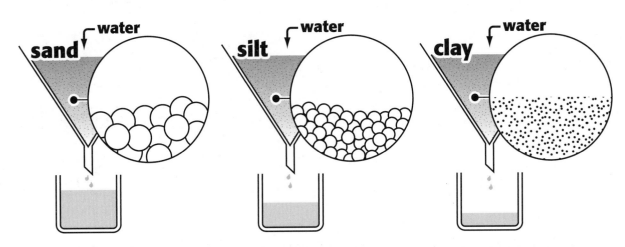

2. **Sand**

   • has the _____ rock particles

   • does not _____ together very well

   • does not _____ water well

   | largest |
   | hold |
   | stick |

   Silt

   • rock particles are _____ than sand but _____ than clay

   • holds _____ water

   • deposited by _____

   | some |
   | larger |
   | rivers |
   | smaller |

   Clay

   • has the _____ rock particles

   • _____ together very well

   • _____ water well

   | smallest |
   | holds |
   | sticks |

ISBN: 978-1-897457-75-7

C. Fill in the blanks to complete the paragraph. Then complete the diagram that shows the ingredients of loam.

clay	water	loam	humus	silt	sand	roots

Most soils have a mixture of 1._____ , 2._____ , and 3._____ . 4._____ , the best soil for plants, is a mixture of rock particles of all different sizes, along with organic material called 5._____ . The decaying plant and animal materials help give the soil structure to hold the plant's 6._____ in place. Loam also holds just the right amount of 7._____ . It lets some water in, while allowing extra to drain.

Ingredients of Loam

◯ : sand ● : silt
• : clay 0 : humus

3 Uses of Soil

Plants make use of soil in more than one way, and different types of soil benefit different plants. We also have different uses for different soils. In this unit, you will see how useful soil is.

After completing this unit, you will

- understand that soil provides food and water for plants.

- understand that the type of soil will determine how soil is used.

This soil is soft, wet, and dark. I think it's good for farming.

Vocabulary

nutrient: substance from food that all living things need in order to grow

mineral: nutrient found in soil

drainage: ability to allow water to empty out

with minerals

without minerals

ISBN: 978-1-897457-75-7

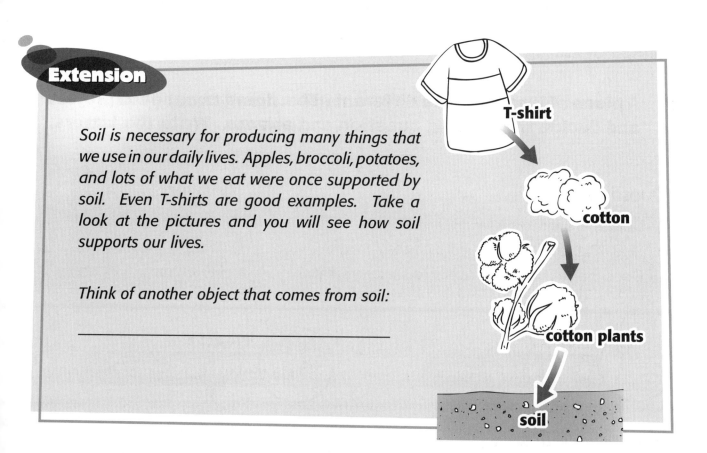

Extension

Soil is necessary for producing many things that we use in our daily lives. Apples, broccoli, potatoes, and lots of what we eat were once supported by soil. Even T-shirts are good examples. Take a look at the pictures and you will see how soil supports our lives.

Think of another object that comes from soil:

_____

T-shirt

cotton

cotton plants

soil

A. Complete the diagram to show how soil supports each product.

grass   leaves   clay   cow   jasmine plants

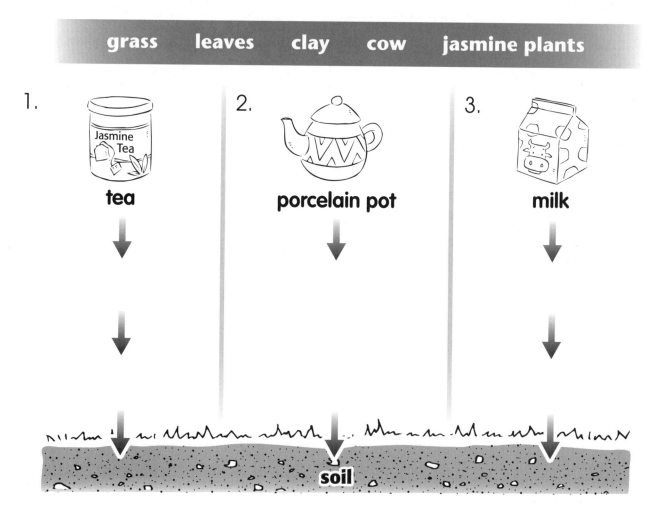

1. tea

2. porcelain pot

3. milk

soil

ISBN: 978-1-897457-75-7

B. A piece of land can have different uses. Read about each project and decide the missing question and answer. Write the letters.

Question

A. Does the soil have lots of humus?

B. Does the soil provide a sturdy base?

C. Does the soil have the ability to stick together?

Answer

D. This is the right spot.

E. Find a spot with clay.

F. Find a sturdy base.

Project A

Build a High-rise

Question

No

Yes

This might be the right spot.

Project B

Start a Garden

Question

No

Maybe I can add humus to the soil.

Yes

Project C

Provide a Soil Source for Pottery Makers

Question

No

Yes

This is the clay I've been looking for.

ISBN: 978-1-897457-75-7

C. Fill in the blanks to complete the paragraph. Then answer the questions.

drainage	water	plants
soil	minerals	place

Almost all plants need 1._____ . Soil contains 2._____ , which gives plants the nutrients they need to live and grow. Different kinds of 3._____ need different amounts of water. Some plants do well with good 4._____ , while others like to keep their "feet" wet. It is soil that helps plants meet their 5._____ needs. Soil also keeps plants in 6._____ , anchoring them to their life-long home.

7. Which plant, the cactus or the tulip, does well in soil with good drainage?

_____

8. What does the word "feet" in the passage mean?

_____

9. Name two things that soil provides for plants.

_____

Introduction

Rock particles are an important part of soil, along with humus, air, and water. Do soils contain more than one kind of particle size? How can we separate the rock particles so we can see how much of each is in the soil?

Hypothesis

Soil can be made up of more than one rock particle size.

Clay, sand, silt, and loam are the four basic kinds of soil.

Materials

- **soil scooped from one area (garden, playground, dirt pile...)**
- **a jar with a lid**
- **water**

Steps

1. Fill about one quarter of the jar with soil.

2. Add water so that the jar is about three quarters full.

ISBN: 978-1-897457-75-7

3. Tighten the lid and shake well.

Shake!

4. Let the jar sit for 2 to 3 hours.

Result

Look at how the soil settles in the jar and draw a picture of the result.

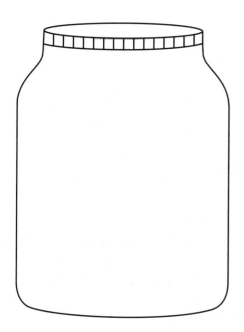

Are there layers?

_____

How many different rock particle sizes do you see?

_____

Conclusion

The hypothesis was: _____

_____

My experiment _____ the
hypothesis.   supported/did not support

ISBN: 978-1-897457-75-7

4 Compost

Composting turns animal and plant waste into a matter that is ideal for fertilizing soil. In this unit, you will see how composting works and what things we can add to our backyard compost.

After completing this unit, you will

- know how composting happens.
- know how we make compost.
- understand the benefits of making compost.

Mandy, it is October now. It took about seven months for our compost to turn into soil.

Vocabulary

compost: a mixture of decaying organic matter

organic: from living or once-living things

decomposer: an organism that breaks down organic materials

decomposers

earwig

woodlice

earthworm

ISBN: 978-1-897457-75-7

Sometimes plants need more nutrients than the soil can give them. When this happens in our gardens, we can buy manure or fertilizer and add it to the soil to make the soil rich in nutrients. This way, plants are healthy and grow to be strong and beautiful. Is there anything else we can add to the soil to make it nutrient-rich? Is there anything we can easily find around us that we do not have to buy?

A. Circle the correct word. Then check the circles to show the composting that happens in nature.

Composting happens wherever **organic / inorganic** material breaks down into a nutrient-rich matter.

Composting in Nature

(A) decaying fish

(B) flowers in bloom

(C) decaying leaves

(D) decaying bird droppings

(E) rotten apples

(F) building a bird nest

B. Fill in the blanks with the given words and check the correct circles.

> decomposers   nutrient-rich   air   organic
> microorganisms   water   compost

Things that are put into composting plants:

- _____ materials

e.g.   Ⓐ fish   Ⓑ grass clippings   Ⓒ wood chips

Ⓓ keys   Ⓔ plastic cups   Ⓕ paper towels

Ⓖ vegetable trimmings

Composting Plant

Ⓗ warm   Ⓘ cold

Ⓙ nine months   Ⓚ five years

Add to organic waste:

- _____
  (keeps it moist)

- _____
  (provides oxygen)

- _____
  (e.g. worms)

- _____
  (e.g. bacteria)

Product:

a dark, crumbly, _____ mixture called _____ which is mainly used in agriculture

      ISBN: 978-1-897457-75-7

C. Fill in the blanks to complete the paragraph. Then check the correct circles and give examples of your own.

meat	reduce	dairy	soil	rodents

Backyard composting helps us 1._____ the amount of waste that goes into the dump. Also, it provides a nutrient-rich 2._____ that we can add to our gardens and lawns. Though 3._____ and 4._____ products can be composted, they should not be included in backyard compost because they attract unwanted 5._____ .

6. Things that can go into compost bins:

From the House:

(A) milk   (B) apple core

(C) seeds   (D) broken glass

(E) newspaper   (F) orange peel

(G) cheese   (H) paper cups

(✔) _____

From the Garden:

(I) soft plant stems

(J) old shovel

(K) grass trimmings

(L) fallen leaves

(✔) _____

5 Living and Non-living Things in Soil

Soil consists of living and non-living things. In this unit, you will look at the living and non-living things in soil and see how they depend on each other.

After completing this unit, you will

- recognize the living and non-living things in soil and their interdependence.
- know that many living things make soil their home.

Teddy, have you said "thank you" to the things in soil that keep our flowers growing?

living things

non-living things

vocabulary

interdependence: depending on each other

larva: young insect

enrich: add good things

absorb: take in and hold

larva

ISBN: 978-1-897457-75-7

Dark, crumbly soil may seem lifeless. However, inside it, there are many living organisms. These organisms eat organic matter by breaking it into tiny pieces. Then, the pieces become valuable nutrients that plants need.

Take a closer look at the soil in your backyard. You may find many little creatures.

A. Check the things that can be found in soil.

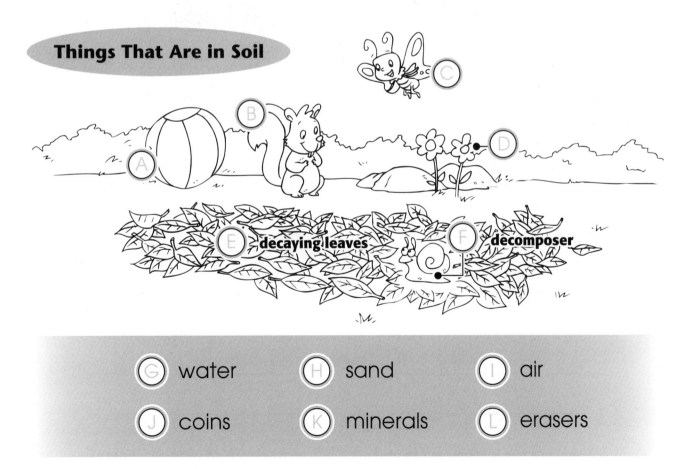

Things That Are in Soil

decaying leaves

decomposer

G water H sand I air

J coins K minerals L erasers

B. Complete the diagram to show how plants and soil depend on each other.

- water
- roots break up hard soil
- keeps plants in place
- nutrients
- decaying plants enrich soil
- roots keep soil from blowing away

Interdependence of
Plants and Soil

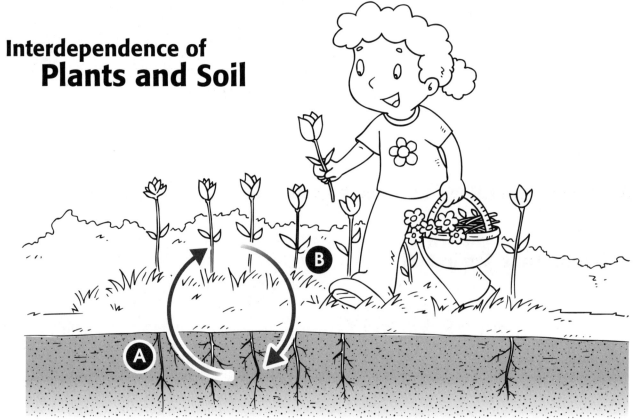

A **Soil to Plants**

_____

_____

_____

_____

B **Plants to Soil**

_____

_____

_____

_____

ISBN: 978-1-897457-75-7

C. Read the paragraph. Then complete the diagram and circle the correct answers.

Earthworms are small creatures that can easily be found in soil, and they are important for growing healthy plants. Earthworms "turn" the soil as they move around in it with their muscular and slimy bodies. They create passages that allow water and air to get into the soil. They also break down organic matter and create humus that plants need to stay healthy.

1.
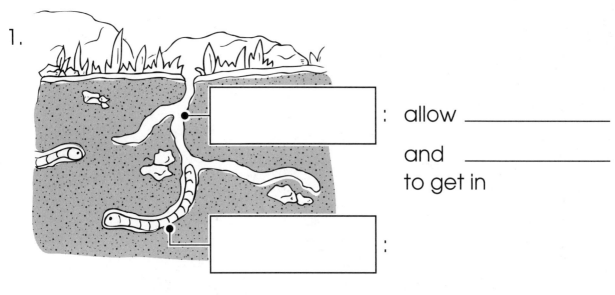

: allow _____

and _____

to get in

:

- breaks down _____ matter

- creates _____ that plants need

2. the body of an earthworm is:

muscular / slimy / rough

3. earthworms break down:

decaying plants / dirt / animal matter

ISBN: 978-1-897457-75-7

6 Soils and Society

Soil is continuously being moved around. Sometimes soil is moved at a rate so slow that we do not notice. At other times, it is moved at an alarming rate that causes the loss of soil. In this unit, you will learn the causes of erosion and how soils affect our lives and the environment.

After completing this unit, you will

- know what things are made of soil.
- understand how natural occurrences cause erosion.
- know how to prevent soil erosion.

Mom, this construction truck can help you remove the soil.

Vocabulary

erosion: the process by which soil is worn away

habitat: environment that gives living things what they need to survive

adobe: clay building material

cement   adobe

ISBN: 978-1-897457-75-7

Making Pottery

Pottery is made of clay that is modelled, dried, and painted into a decorative object. However, pottery is not only decorative art; it can also be a practical item for everyday use.

Steps to Make Pottery:

1. Shape the clay.
2. Bake to dry it.
3. Paint it.

Done!

Can you think of other things that are made of clay?

A. Check the things that are made of soil. Then give one example.

Things That Are Made of Soil

mud hut Ⓐ

car Ⓑ

adobe home Ⓒ

Ⓓ sun   Ⓔ bricks   Ⓕ ceramic plates

Ⓖ clay pots   Ⓗ baskets   ✔ _____

B. Fill in the blanks with the given words.

Erosion Is Caused by...

human activities	natural events	
glaciers	water	farming
construction	wind	rain

1. [ ]

   a. _____ blows and carries the soil away.

   b. Heavy_____ carries soil down a mountain.

   c. _____ carry soil across the land as the ice moves.

   d. Moving _____ removes the soil from the riverbanks.

2. [ ]

   a. _____ involves the removal of topsoil.

   b. Poor _____ practices make the ground's surface soil bare, which speeds up erosion.

ISBN: 978-1-897457-75-7

C. Read the paragraph. Then label the diagram and write how each prevents erosion.

Human activities can speed up soil erosion, making it happen too quickly for the natural environment to handle. Fortunately, there are many things that we are doing to slow down this process. Here are some of them: plant **vegetation** because plant roots help hold soil in place; cover soil with **mulch** to protect it from getting washed or blown away; and build **windbreaks**, which are rows of trees planted along the edge of a farm that prevent wind from eroding the soil.

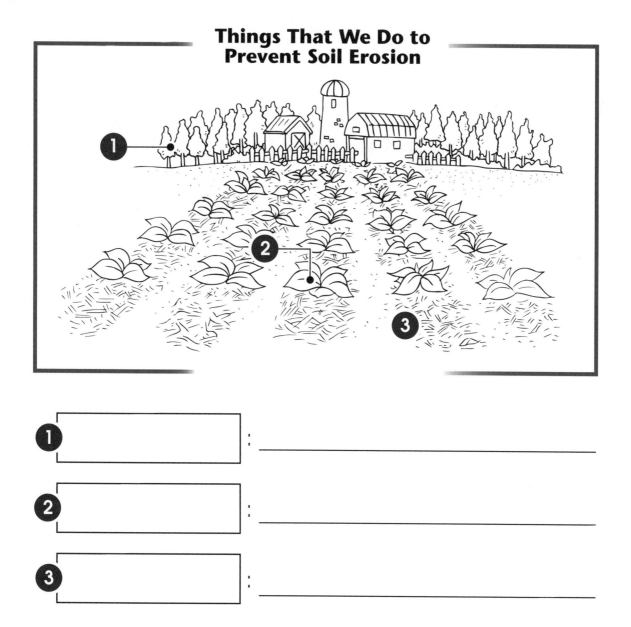

Things That We Do to Prevent Soil Erosion

1 _____ : _____

2 _____ : _____

3 _____ : _____

ISBN: 978-1-897457-75-7

Experiment

Introduction

Moving water is one of the natural forces that can cause soil erosion. People are looking for different ways to prevent soil erosion. Do you think that planting plants in soil can prevent the topsoil from being washed away?

Hypothesis

Predict what will happen to grassy soil and soil with no plants when water is added.

_____

_____

Steps

Part 1

1. Fill both sandwich boxes with soil. Plant grass seeds in one of them.

2. Water both boxes of soil daily.

Materials

- *soil*
- *grass seeds*
- *two sandwich boxes*
- *a spray bottle*
- *a cup*

ISBN: 978-1-897457-75-7

When the grass is about 3 cm tall, go to part 2.

Grassy Soil

Bare Soil

Part 2

1. Spray the grassy soil and bare soil with the spray bottle.

The soil that is less likely to get washed away is the:

○ grassy soil   ○ bare soil

2. Water the grassy soil and bare soil with the cup.

The soil that is less likely to get washed away is the:

○ grassy soil   ○ bare soil

Conclusion

The hypothesis was: _____

_____

My experiment _____ the hypothesis.

supported/did not support

Try to complete this review in **30 minutes**.

30 minutes

This review consists of five sections, from A to E. The marks for each question are shown in parentheses. The circle at the bottom right corner is for the marks you get in each section. An overall record is on the last page of the review.

A. Write T for true and F for false.

1. Air can be found in soil. **(2)** _____

2. Clay holds water better than sand. **(2)** _____

3. Bones are perfect for backyard compost. **(2)**

   _____

4. Windbreaks prevent water from eroding the soil. **(2)**

   _____

8

ISBN: 978-1-897457-75-7

B. Do the matching.

1. 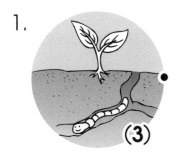 (3)

2. 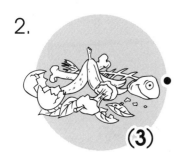 (3)

3. 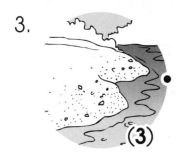 (3)

- organic waste

- decomposer

- soil with the largest rock particles

- prevents soil erosion

- made of soil

4.  (3)

5.  (3)

15

ISBN: 978-1-897457-75-7

C. **Look at the results of the experiment. Identify the soil samples and match them with the correct descriptions.**

Experiment: The same amount of water is poured into each soil sample – **sand, clay,** and **silt**.

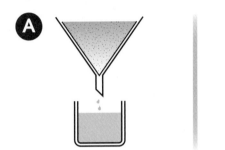 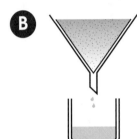 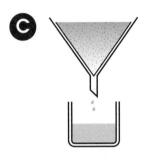

1. **Soil Sample**   **Description**

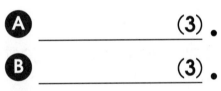

Ⓐ _____ **(3)** .

Ⓑ _____ **(3)** .

Ⓒ _____ **(3)** .

- holds water very well **(2)**

- deposited by rivers **(2)**

- sticks together very well **(2)**

- has the largest rock particles **(2)**

2. Name the best soil for plants and write its ingredients. Explain why it is better than the soils listed above for gardening.

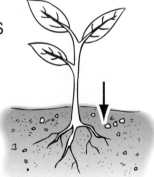

The best soil for plants: _____ **(2)**

Its ingredients: _____ **(4)**

Reason: _____

_____ **(6)**

ISBN: 978-1-897457-75-7

D. Fill in the blanks and answer the questions.

minerals   air   acid   organic matter   water   fire

1. **Substances of Soil**

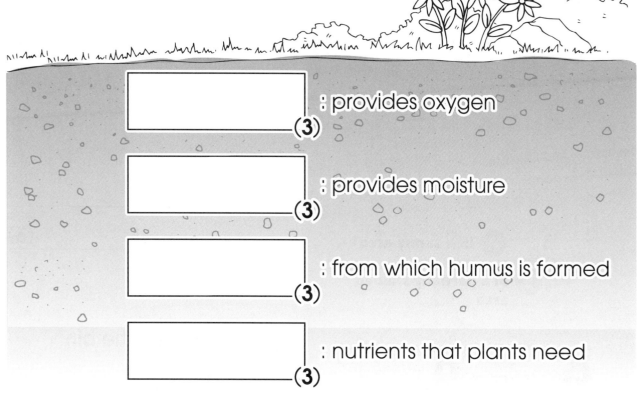

: provides oxygen **(3)**

: provides moisture **(3)**

: from which humus is formed **(3)**

: nutrients that plants need **(3)**

2. What does compost have that can enrich soil? **(3)**

   Ⓐ nutrients   Ⓑ water   Ⓒ air

3. What determines the amount of water soil can hold? **(3)**

   Ⓐ weight   Ⓑ colour   Ⓒ rock particle size

4. Why is it important to loosen up soil before planting? **(3)**

   Ⓐ It breaks up rock particles and creates minerals.

   Ⓑ It allows more air and water to get into the soil.

21

ISBN: 978-1-897457-75-7

E. **Choose the best option for each pair and give a reason for your choice. Then answer the questions.**

How to Compost

1.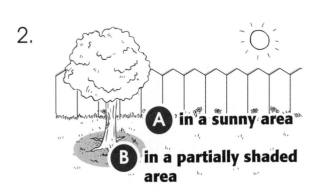

Compost bin: _____ **(2)** ;

_____

_____ **(3)**

2.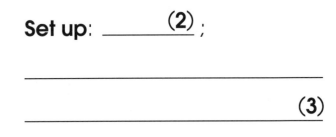

Set up: _____ **(2)** ;

_____

_____ **(3)**

3.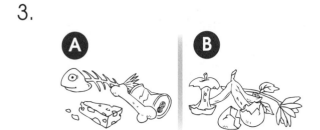

Things to put into the bin:

_____ **(2)** ; _____

_____ **(3)**

4. What four things are needed for the process of composting? **(4)**

_____

5. Name and describe the product of composting. Then write what it is used for. **(8)**

_____

_____

27

ISBN: 978-1-897457-75-7

My Record

Section A	8
Section B	15
Section C	29
Section D	21
Section E	27

Total

100

80-100

Great work! You really understand your science stuff! Research your favourite science topics at the library or on the Internet to find out more about the topics related to this section. Keep challenging yourself to learn more!

60-79

Good work! You understand some basic concepts, but try reading through the units again to see whether you can master the material! Go over the questions that you had trouble with to make sure you know the correct answers.

below 60

You can do much better! Try reading over the units again. Ask your parents or teachers any questions you might have. Once you feel confident that you know the material, try the review again. Science is exciting, so don't give up!

The Pedologist

Do you like to dig in the dirt and examine the soil's colour, texture, and inhabitants? If so, pedology may be for you. Pedology is an area of science concerned with studying soils. Pedologists study soil's properties, how soil is formed, how living things interact with it, and how human activities affect soil. They classify soil, examine the effects pollution has on it, and decide how to maintain good soil conditions for the benefit of plant life and for agriculture. Many pedologists work in the fields of agriculture and ecology.

Vasily Dokuchaev was a Russian scientist born in 1846. He created the first soil classification system by studying how different soils were formed and why they were different, and then writing all the information down so others could use it to classify soil. He is considered by many to be the father of pedology.

ISBN: 978-1-897457-75-7

Cool Science Facts

1 Do you know that sand makes sound?

2 Can you take a bath in sand?

3 What makes the mud from the Dead Sea different from other mud?

4 Is there any plant on the moon?

5 Pottery is made of clay. Then, what is glass made of?

Find the answers on the next page.

ISBN: 978-1-897457-75-7

Cool Science Facts

1 Some sand dunes in deserts or along shorelines make sounds. How these sounds are made is still a mystery to scientists. However, it is produced by wind passing over these dunes. Some dunes are musical, as they sing and whistle, while some bark and croak, sounding like a frog!

Ding...Ding...Ding...

Croak...

Woof?

2 In Japan, the people in a region bury themselves from neck to toe in hot sand that is found near hot springs. They believe that the hot sand helps release waste from their bodies by making them sweat.

ISBN: 978-1-897457-75-7

4 There is no air or water, the two essential things that plants need, on the moon. Hence, there is no plant on the moon.

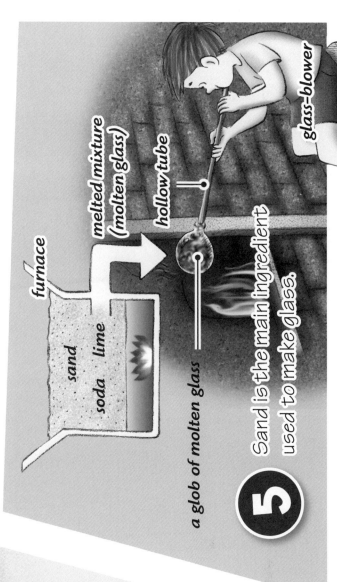

5 Sand is the main ingredient used to make glass.

- furnace
- sand
- soda   lime
- melted mixture (molten glass)
- hollow tube
- a glob of molten glass
- glass–blower

3 Due to the evaporation of water in the Dead Sea over thousands of years, the salt and minerals have been absorbed in the mud as the body of water is drying out. As a result, the mud has a much higher mineral content and salt concentration than other mud.

DEAD SEA

ISBN: 978-1-897457-75-7

ISBN: 978-1-897457-75-7

Answers

ISBN: 978-1-897457-75-7

Answers

Section 1

1 Plants and Their Needs

A.

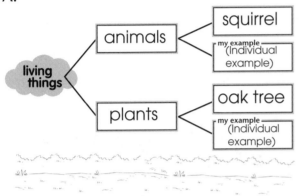

B. a Plant: B, C, E, H, M
Both: A, K, L
an Animal: D, F, G, I, J

C. Plants Need: light, air, water, space, warmth, food
1. light 2. air
3. water 4. warmth
5. food

D.1a. stem: can store lots of water; some can even absorb water from the air
b. spines: protect the cactus against animals; provide some shade for the stem
c. roots: grow quickly after a rainfall; spread wide and shallow to collect as much water as possible
2. (Suggested result)
The paper towel under the paper should be drier than the one under the wax paper.

2 Parts of Plants

A. water ; minerals
anchor
single ; dandelion
spreading ; monocot

B. 1. nutrients
2. food
3. water
(Suggested answer)
small and prickly
4. thorns
(Suggested answer)
wide and flat
5. winds
(Suggested answer)
wide and flat
6. covered
(Suggested answer)
thin and prickly

C. Pistil ; ovary
Stamen
Petal ; flower
Ovary ; seeds
Sepal ; base
Pollination ; pollen ; Pollinators

D. 1. woody ; 3 metres ; 10 centimetres ; tree ; shrub
2. broadleaf ; conifer ; broadleaf
3. (Suggested answers)
Broadleaf Trees
Characteristics: have wide, flat leaves ; produce flowers
Examples: birch, oak
Conifer Trees
Characteristics: have needle-like leaves ; produce seed cones
Examples: cedar, pine

ISBN: 978-1-897457-75-7

3 Plant Survival

A. Animal Pollination: B ;
strong ; sweet ; bright ; animals
Wind Pollination: A ;
small ; no ; not colourful ; wind

B. turns ; B
stores ; D
defends ; A
appears ; C

C. 1. ground
2. top
3. float
4. Rainforest

D. 1. mangrove
2. coconut
3. blackberry
4. burdock
5. dandelion
6. maple
7. by water
8. by animal
9. by wind

E. 1. (Suggested examples)
by wind ; maple
by water ; mangrove
by animal ; blackberry
by gravity ; calabash vine
mechanical dispersal; pea plant

2. When a pea pod dries out, its two
seams split and release its seeds.
Check: A

3. (Suggested answer)
The fruit is heavy so that it will fall
to the ground.

Experiment

(Suggested experiment outcome)
Result:
The carnation turned out the same
colour as the food colouring. This is
because the coloured water travelled
up the stem and to the white flower.
Conclusion:
Water moves up a plant's stem. ;
supported

4 Plant Growth

A.

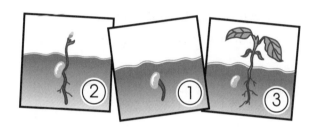

root ; water
shoot
leaves ; germination

B. Yes ; No ; No ; Yes
water ; warmth ; food ; sunlight

C. 1. soil
2. germinates
3. leaves
4. tree
5. flowers ; fruit
6. seed
7. life cycle

D. 1.

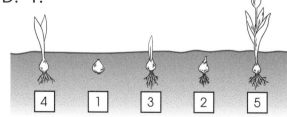

2. It is a modified stem that stores nutrients for a plant.

3. Onions are examples of edible bulbs. Lilies are examples of spring flowering bulbs.

4. A spring flowering bulb begins to grow in the spring with water and warm weather.

5. The bulb provides nutrients.

6. Bulbs bloom much more quickly than seeds do.

5 How We Use Plants

A. oxygen ; carbon dioxide
carbon dioxide ; oxygen

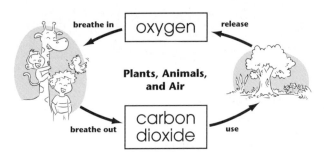

B.

C.

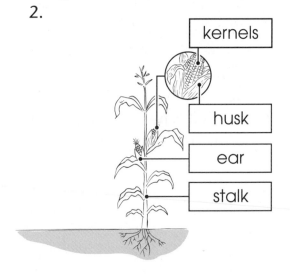

D. (Suggested examples)
1. shelter ; wooden staircase ; wooden door
2. medicine ; garlic (natural antibiotic) ; ginger (settles stomach)
3. food ; bread ; carrots
4. clothing ; rubber (from sap) ; cotton
5. paper ; matches
6. for shelter ; beavers build beaver lodges from tree branches
for food ; deer eat leaves and grass

E. 1. in the past: cornmeal (bread, pudding, syrup) ; other foods (soup, popcorn) ; masks ; bags ; baskets ; mats ; dolls ; moccasins ; fuel
in the present: major food source ; fuel ; insulation ; material in tires ; rayon

2.

6 Protecting Plants

A. Check: flooding ; extreme temperatures ; drought ; wildfires ; tornadoes

B. A: Activity: farming
   Description: Forests are cleared to make fields for crops.
   B: Activity: construction
   Impact: loss of marsh habitat
   C: Activity: factories
   Impact: trees die
   D: Activity: gardening
   Description: Invasive, non-native plants are planted.

C. Check: A, B, C
   (Suggested answer)
   They provide us with the oxygen we need to breathe.

D. 1. fruit
   2. plants
   3. plants
   4. plants ; different

E. 1. Wild Columbine:
   (Colour with red and yellow)
   May ; June
   10 to 50 cm
   moist soil
   some sun and some shade
   Black-eyed Susan:
   (Colour with yellow and brown)
   from June to July
   up to 50 cm
   dry to moist soil
   lots of sunlight

   2. Native plants support the insects, birds, and other animals in a habitat. They often do not need to be watered or fertilized.

Experiment

(Individual experiment outcome)

Review

A. 1. T   2. F
   3. F   4. T

B. 1.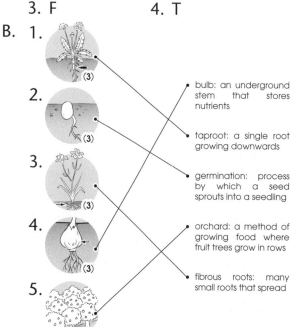
   2.
   3.
   4.
   5.

- bulb: an underground stem that stores nutrients
- taproot: a single root growing downwards
- germination: process by which a seed sprouts into a seedling
- orchard: a method of growing food where fruit trees grow in rows
- fibrous roots: many small roots that spread

C.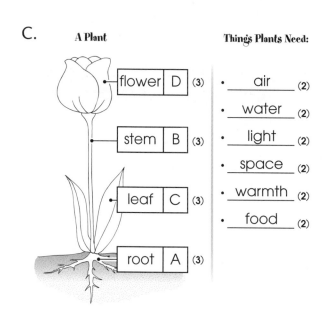

A Plant

flower D (3)
stem B (3)
leaf C (3)
root A (3)

Things Plants Need:
- air (2)
- water (2)
- light (2)
- space (2)
- warmth (2)
- food (2)

D. 1. A: pistil ; Pollen reaches the ovary through this stalk.

ISBN: 978-1-897457-75-7

Answers

B: stamen ; This is the pollen-producing part.

C: petal ; This part protects the flower and attracts pollinators.

D: ovary ; Seeds form here if pollination occurs.

E: sepal ; It covered the flower when the flower was a bud.

2. has strong scent ; has sweet nectar ; is brightly coloured

E. 1. food

(Individual examples)

shelter

(Individual examples)

2. A seed is buried in well-watered soil and germinates. It continues to grow until it becomes a tree. Then it produces flowers. The flowers fall off the tree and the cherry fruit develops.

3. (Suggested answer)

Factories cause air pollution, which causes acid rain. This rain then falls on trees, killing them.

Section 2

1 Structures

A.

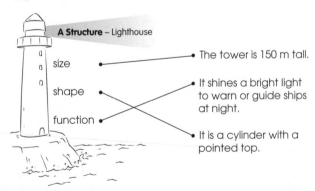

B. 1. fence ; long ; rectangular
2. house ; big ; box
3. water tower ; big ; round
4. tracks ; long ; flat

C. 1. animal-made
2. human-made
3. spiderweb ; fishing net ; to catch prey

anthill ; skyscraper ; to provide shelter

beaver dam ; hydro dam ; to control water flow

mole burrow ; subway tunnel ; to travel underground

D. 1.

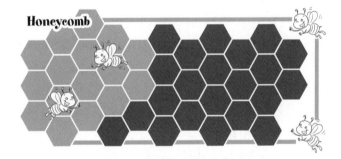

animal-made ; bees

hexagonal

wax

house larvae ; store honey and pollen

2. It ensures that the least amount of material is used to create the largest amount of storage, so the bees use less wax.

3. Bees need honey to produce wax.

2 Forces Acting on Structures

A. 1. push

Check: B

2. pull

Check: A

ISBN: 978-1-897457-75-7

B. 1. compression   2. tension

3.

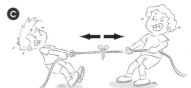

A	compression
B	tension
C	tension

C. 1. push ; moves
2. push ; changes shape
3. pull ; changes shape
4. push ; changes direction
5. push ; changes shape
6. pull ; changes direction

D. 1a. push
b. push ; pull
c. push
2.

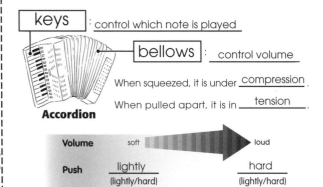

keys : control which note is played

bellows : control volume

When squeezed, it is under compression .

When pulled apart, it is in tension .

Accordion

Volume	soft	loud
Push	lightly	hard
	(lightly/hard)	(lightly/hard)

3 Strength and Stability

A.

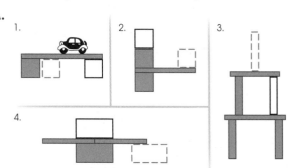

B. 1. stability ; strength
2. stability ; strength

C.

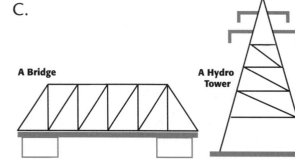

A Bridge   **A Hydro Tower**

Triangles

D.

1.

Ⓐ longer legs
☑ lower centre of gravity

2.

☑ more stability from triangles
Ⓑ more flexibility from triangles

3.

Reason: more stability from tent lines

4.

Reason: more stability from wider base

ISBN: 978-1-897457-75-7

E. 1. A tightrope walker carries a pole that bends downwards at its ends. He or she gains stability by lowering his or her centre of gravity.
   2. Check: B
   3. (Suggested answer)
   Add weights to both ends.
   (Individual drawing)

Experiment

(Individual experiment outcome)

4   Structures and Materials

A. 1. durable ; Brick
   2. flexible ; Plastic
   3. strong ; Steel
B. (Suggested properties)
   1. Check: A
   lightweight and easy to carry ; foldable
   2. Check: C
   easy to clean ; resilient surface to minimize injuries and to provide grip
   3. Check: A
   strong ; durable
C. A: adding layers ; strength
   B: braiding ; strength
   C: folding ; stability
   D: adding layers ; strength
D. 1. tipi
   Aboriginal peoples
   Canadian prairies
   animal skins
   durable, waterproof, abundant

2. adobe house
   Pueblo people
   southwestern United States
   mud bricks
   keep the air inside the house cool
3. igloo
   Inuit people
   the Arctic
   blocks of snow
   abundant, traps heat

5   Bridges

A. 1. Check: A, B, D, E
   2. Check: A, D, E
   3. Check: A, C, D
B.

1.    Beam ; beam

2. 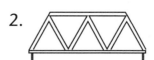   Truss ; triangular

3. 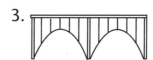   Arch ; arch

4.

Suspension ; cables

ISBN: 978-1-897457-75-7

C.

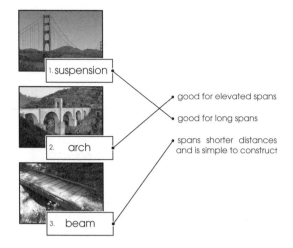

1. suspension — good for elevated spans

2. arch — good for long spans

3. beam — spans shorter distances and is simple to construct

4. (Individual answers)

D. 1. truss ; Québec City
   the lower Saint Lawrence River
   987 metres
   1919

2. suspension
   San Francisco Bay
   San Francisco to northern California
   2737 metres
   1937

3. arch ; Shanghai, China
   the Huangpu River
   3900 metres
   2003

6 **Structures and Us**

A. 1a. destruction ; negative
   b. more ; positive
   2a. disrupting ; negative
   b. providing ; positive

B.

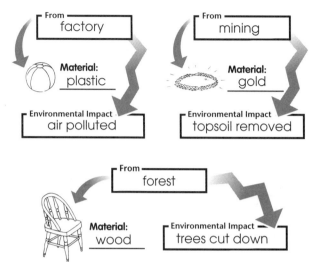

From factory
Material: plastic
Environmental Impact: air polluted

From mining
Material: gold
Environmental Impact: topsoil removed

From forest
Material: wood
Environmental Impact: trees cut down

C. (Suggested answers)
1. A strong and stable bridge carries traffic safely.
2. Strong and durable plastic ware does not break down easily.
3. Water pipes are reliable and we are sure we have a water supply all the time.

D. 1.

Beijing

China

Great Wall of China
total length: 8851 km

2. The purpose was to defend China against invaders.
3. The materials used include earth packed into blocks, stones, and bricks.
4. Those materials were abundant.
5. Brick is found most often because it is a very durable material.

ISBN: 978-1-897457-75-7

Answers

6. Natural forces and attacks by humans caused damage.

Experiment
(Individual experiment outcome)

Review
A. 1. F   2. F
   3. F   4. T

B.

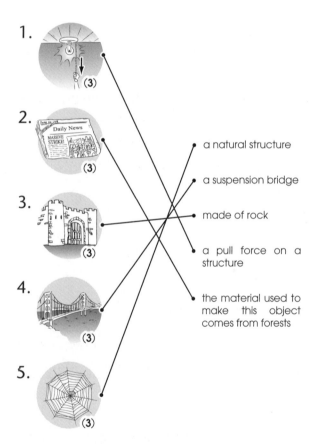

1.
2.
3.
4.
5.

- a natural structure
- a suspension bridge
- made of rock
- a pull force on a structure
- the material used to make this object comes from forests

C.1a. truss
   b. Triangular trusses are added.
   c. They are under compression.
 2a. suspension
   b. Cables are attached to the towers.
   c. They will be in tension.

D. 1. cardboard
   2. lightweight; holds its shape
   3. folding
   4. the loss of trees
   5. to protect the eggs and prevent them from rolling around
   6. bird's nest ; small, round

E. 1. Check: A, B, D
   (Individual example)
   2. compression
   3. changes shape
   4. water
   5. a pushing force

Section 3

1 Force: Push or Pull
A. 1. push   2. pull
   3. pull   4. push
B. 1. pull   2. push
   3. pull   4. push
   5. push   6. pull
   7. push and pull
   8. push
   9. push and pull
  10. push and pull
C. (Suggested answers)
   1. catching a ball thrown to you ; applying different forces on a moving cart with your hands
   2. bringing a sled up a hill ; pulling a moving cart back to you ; pulling a wagon around a corner

ISBN: 978-1-897457-75-7

2 Contact and Non-contact Forces

A. Circle: pulling
   Check: A, B, C, D

B. 1. moving water ; contact
   2. wind ; non-contact
   3. gravity ; non-contact
   4. buoyancy ; contact
   5. friction ; contact
   6. muscular ; contact
   7. magnetic ; non-contact
   8. electrostatic ; non-contact

C. 1. south
   2a. repel
    b. attract
    3. iron, steel, or nickel
    4. (Suggested answer)
       fridge magnets and paper clip holders

3 Forces and Movement

A.

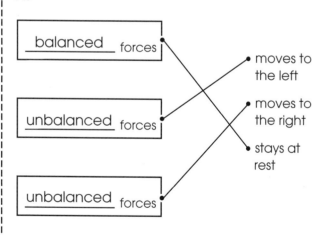

B. A: change direction
   B: start
   C: speed up
   D: remain at rest
   E: stop

C. 1. T
   2. T
   3. T
   4.

Experiment

(Individual experiment outcome)

4 Friction

A. force ; opposite ; stop ; contact ; greater

B.

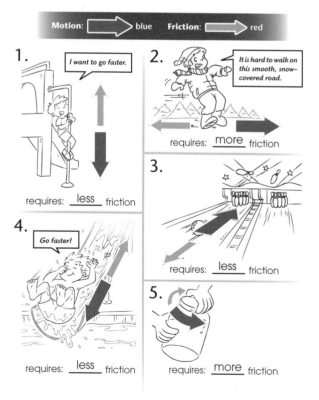

C. 1.

dry , rough
surface

a lot of friction

smooth or icy
surface

a little friction

2. Winter tires should be used in the winter because they have special grooves to increase friction in snowy or icy conditions.

5 Forces in Nature

A. 1. hurricane
2. lightning
3. moving water
4. buoyancy
5. magnetism

B.

volcanic eruption   flood   tornado

lightning   earthquake   landslide

Check: cause erosion ; destroy houses and buildings ; destroy natural habitats (Suggested answer)
cause air and water pollution

C. 1.

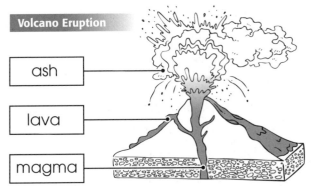

Volcano Eruption

ash

lava

magma

2. Magma is found deep down below the Earth's surface. It contains minerals.
3. The lava and ash from volcanic eruptions break down into soil that is perfect for farming.

6 Forces in Our Lives

A. B ; A ; D ; C

B. 1a.

b.

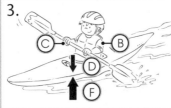

c.

2.

3.

4.

C. 1. A: 45 m   B: 80 m

ISBN: 978-1-897457-75-7

2. They are used for producing electricity by harnessing wind force with huge turbines.

3. over 100

4. B

Experiment

(Individual experiment outcome)

Review

A. 1. T   2. F
   3. T   4. T

B.

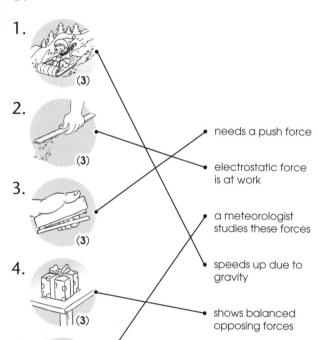

1.
2.
3.
4.
5.

needs a push force

electrostatic force is at work

a meteorologist studies these forces

speeds up due to gravity

shows balanced opposing forces

C. 1.

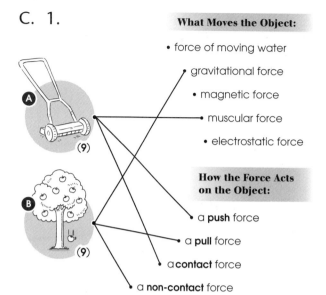

What Moves the Object:

• force of moving water

  gravitational force

• magnetic force

  muscular force

• electrostatic force

How the Force Acts on the Object:

a **push** force

a **pull** force

a **contact** force

a **non-contact** force

2a. slows down
  b. friction

D. 1. to the left
   2. unbalanced forces
   3. remain at rest
   4. balanced forces
   5. opposite directions

E. 1.

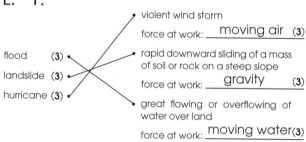

flood   (3)
landslide (3)
hurricane (3)

violent wind storm
force at work: ___moving air___ (3)

rapid downward sliding of a mass of soil or rock on a steep slope
force at work: ___gravity___ (3)

great flowing or overflowing of water over land
force at work: ___moving water___(3)

2. A: electrostatic force
   B: friction
   C: muscular force
   D: gravity
   E: buoyancy

ISBN: 978-1-897457-75-7

Section 4

1 Soil

A. Check: A ; B ; C ; D ; F ; H

B. 1. D   2. C
    3. B   4. A
    5. E

C. 1. inorganic
    2. water
    3. Organic
    4. earthworms
    5. minerals
    6. organic: A ; B ; D ; G
       inorganic: C ; E ; F

2 Kinds of Soil

A. 1. sand
    2. clay
    3. (Individual answer)

B. 1.

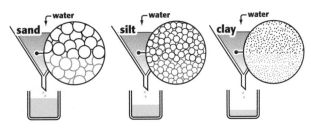

    2. largest ; stick ; hold
       smaller ; larger ; some ; rivers
       smallest ; sticks ; holds

C. 1. sand
    2. silt
    3. clay
    4. Loam
    5. humus
    6. roots
    7. water

3 Uses of Soil

A.

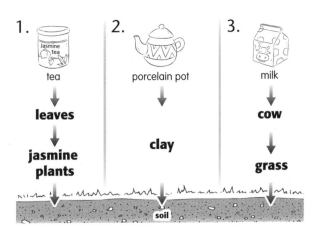

B.

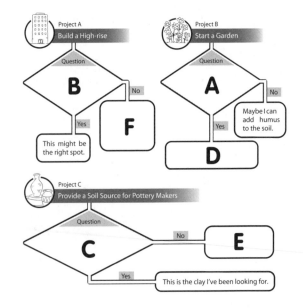

C. 1. soil
2. minerals
3. plants
4. drainage
5. water
6. place
7. the cactus
8. roots
9. (Any two of the following)
water, nutrients, home

Experiment

(Individual experiment outcome)

4 Compost

A. organic
Check: A ; C ; D ; E
B. organic
Check: A ; B ; C ; F ; G
Check: H ; J
Add to organic waste: water ; air ;
decomposers ; microorganisms
Product: nutrient-rich ; compost
C. 1. reduce
2. soil
3. meat
4. dairy
5. rodents
6. Check: B ; C ; E ; F ; H
(Individual example)
Check: I ; K ; L
(Individual example)

5 Living and Non-living Things in Soil

A. Check: E ; F ; G ; H ; I ; K
B. A: water ; nutrients ; keeps plants in place
B: roots break up hard soil ; decaying plants enrich soil ; roots keep soil from blowing away
C. 1.

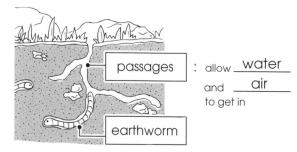

: allow __water__ and __air__ to get in

• breaks down __organic__ matter
• creates __humus__ that plants need

2. muscular ; slimy
3. decaying plants ; animal matter

6 Soils and Society

A. Check: A ; C ; E ; F ; G
(Individual example)
B. 1. natural events
a. Wind
b. rain
c. Glaciers
d. water
2. human activities
a. Construction
b. farming
C. 1. windbreak: prevents wind from eroding the soil
2. vegetation: the roots help hold soil in place
3. mulch: protects soil from getting washed or blown away

ISBN: 978-1-897457-75-7

Experiment
(Individual experiment outcome)

Review

A. 1. T   2. T
   3. F   4. F

B.

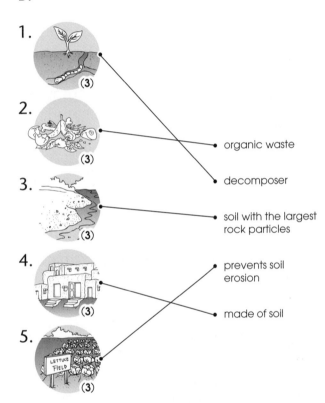

1.
2.
3.
4.
5.

- organic waste
- decomposer
- soil with the largest rock particles
- prevents soil erosion
- made of soil

C. 1.

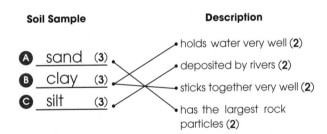

Soil Sample	Description
A sand (3)	holds water very well (2)
B clay (3)	deposited by rivers (2)
C silt (3)	sticks together very well (2)
	has the largest rock particles (2)

2. loam
sand, silt, clay, humus
It provides soil structure to hold roots in place and contains nutrients. It also holds just the right amount of water.

D. 1.

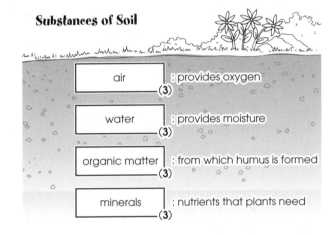

Substances of Soil

air	: provides oxygen (3)
water	: provides moisture (3)
organic matter	: from which humus is formed (3)
minerals	: nutrients that plants need (3)

2. A

3. C

4. B

E. 1. A ; The gaps allow air to get into the compost.

2. B ; A partially shaded area helps keep the compost moist and the heat from the sun helps speed up the composting process.

3. B ; Organic waste should be put in the bin, but meat and dairy products will attract rodents.

4. Decomposers, microorganisms, air, and water are needed.

5. It is called compost, which is a dark, crumbly, and nutrient-rich matter that is used to enrich soil.

TRIVIA

· Questions ·

ISBN: 978-1-897457-75-7

ISBN: 978-1-897457-75-7

True or False

Glass is always transparent.

About how many times does lightning strike the Earth in one minute?

A. 6
B. 600
C. 6000

What is the tallest living organism on Earth?

California redwood tree

giraffe

CN Tower

True or False

The Earth is the only planet that has a moon.

ISBN: 978-1-897457-75-7

Answer:

false

Frosted glass is translucent.

Answer:

California redwood tree

It can reach heights of 115 m. That is like 20 giraffes standing on top of one another.

Answer:

C. 6000

Answer:

false

All planets have moons except Mercury and Venus.

ISBN: 978-1-897457-75-7

What causes Jack to pop out?

A. push force
B. pull force
C. box force
D. spring force

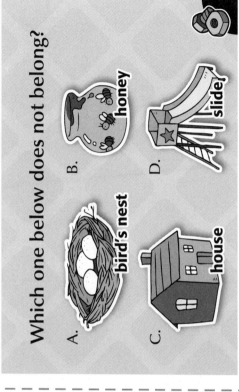

Which one below does not belong?

A. bird's nest
B. honey
C. house
D. slide

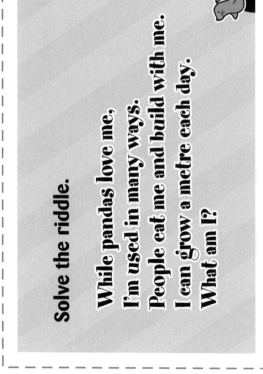

Solve the riddle.

While pandas love me,
I'm used in many ways.
People eat me and build with me.
I can grow a metre each day.
What am I?

True or False

Rivers always flow downhill.

ISBN: 978-1-897457-75-7

Answer:

A. push force

Answer:

bamboo

Answer:

B. honey

The rest are structures.

Answer:

true

Rivers always flow downhill because gravity pulls the water downwards.

ISBN: 978-1-897457-75-7

True or False

Like humans, plants stop growing at a certain age.

For about how long can a tree live in a city?

A. 50 years

B. 1 year

C. 8 years

Which one is bigger: the sun or the moon?

True or False

Rain falls into lakes, so all lakes contain fresh water.

ISBN: 978-1-897457-75-7

Answer:

false

Plants grow throughout their lives.

Answer:

the sun

The sun is 400 times bigger than the moon. They appear to be about the same size because the sun is much farther away from the Earth than the moon.

Answer:

C. 8 years

While trees can live for a very long time, they need favourable conditions to grow. Cities do not provide these conditions.

Answer:

false

Most lakes contain fresh water, but some are salt water lakes, like Redberry Lake in Saskatchewan.

ISBN: 978-1-897457-75-7

This tool was called screwturner when it was first invented. What is it called now?

A. driving wheel
B. screwdriver
C. bolt
D. screw

How old is the world's oldest tree?

A. 9550 years old
B. 1055 years old
C. 875 years old

Happy Birthday!

True or False

When snow melts, it disappears forever.

What is the largest living thing on Earth?

A. a tree
B. a blue whale
C. a mushroom

ISBN: 978-1-897457-75-7

Answer:

B. screwdriver

Answer:

false

When snow melts, it becomes water. It does not disappear.

Answer:

A. 9550 years old

The oldest recorded tree is a spruce tree in Sweden.

Answer:

C. a mushroom

This underground mushroom was found in Oregon, United States. It is so big that it could cover almost 1665 football fields!

ISBN: 978-1-897457-75-7

For how long can a seed be carried by wind?

A. several minutes

B. several hours

C. several days

Which utensil was invented last?

Which force causes rug burn?

A. gravitational force

B. frictional force

C. rug force

D. pull force

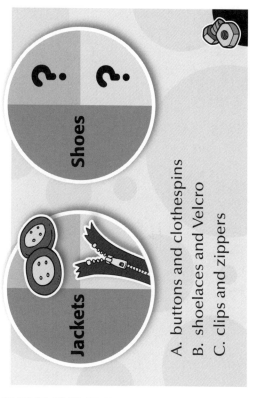

Jackets

Shoes

A. buttons and clothespins

B. shoelaces and Velcro

C. clips and zippers

ISBN: 978-1-897457-75-7

Answer:

C. several days

A light cottonwood tree seed covered in white, fluffy hair stays in flight the longest of any seed carried by wind.

Answer:

B. frictional force

Answer:

fork

Before forks were invented, people ate with their hands.

Answer:

B. shoelaces and Velcro

They are both fasteners for shoes.

ISBN: 978-1-897457-75-7

True or False

Some plants are carnivorous.

How long does it take for 2 cm of topsoil to form?

A. 5 months
B. 5 years
C. 500 years

True or False

Mercury is the only metal that is in liquid form at room temperature.

Solve the riddle.

I grow on a palm tree.
I am hard as a stone.
Inside I am white as snow.
What am I?

ISBN: 978-1-897457-75-7

Answer:

true

Some plants, such as the Venus Fly Trap, are carnivorous. They trap insects and digest them.

Answer:

true

Answer:

C. 500 years

Answer:

a coconut

ISBN: 978-1-897457-75-7

What is the highest temperature recorded in Canada?

A. 30°C
B. 45°C
C. 70°C

A space shuttle travels faster than sound but slower than light.

True or False

In 1976, the CN Tower became the tallest building in the world. For how long did it hold this record?

A. 10 months
B. 31 years
C. 102 years

Trees are the largest kind of plant.

True or False

ISBN: 978-1-897457-75-7

Answer:

B. 45°C

This temperature was recorded in Saskatchewan in 1937.

Answer:

true

Answer:

B. 31 years

The CN Tower lost its record to a building in Dubai in 2007.

Answer:

true

There are trees that are taller than a 15-storey building.

ISBN: 978-1-897457-75-7

At which point would less force be needed to lift the elephant?

Tess waters her plant every few days and keeps it outside under her porch where it gets lots of fresh air. But Tess's plant is dying. What might Tess's plant not be getting enough of?

Brakes are to cars as _____ are to passengers.

A. cup holders

B. headlights

C. seatbelts

About how many stars in the night sky can you see with your naked eye?

A. 2

B. 2000

C. 2 000 000

ISBN: 978-1-897457-75-7

Answer:
point B

Answer:
C. seatbelts

Answer:
sunlight

Answer:
B. 2000

ISBN: 978-1-897457-75-7

True or False

The amount of water there is on Earth is less than the amount there was a thousand years ago.

What is metal most attracted to?

True or False

Mushrooms are plants.

How many days of rain a year does the rainiest place in the world have?

A. 10
B. 30
C. 350

ISBN: 978-1-897457-75-7

Answer:

false

The Earth has always had the same amount of water.

Answer:

a magnet

Answer:

false

Mushrooms are neither plants nor animals. They are fungi.

Answer:

C. 350

Mt. Waialeale in Hawaii has more rainy days than any other place in the world.

ISBN: 978-1-897457-75-7

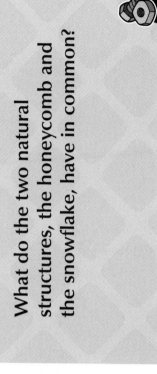

Does sound travel faster in air or in water?

What do the two natural structures, the honeycomb and the snowflake, have in common?

How many species of bacteria are there in one gram of soil?

A. more than 5000

B. 50

C. 1

True or False

A kite and a sailboat use the same kind of force to move.

ISBN: 978-1-897457-75-7

Answer:

in water

Sound travels about 4 times faster in water than in air.

Answer:

A. more than 5000

There are 5000 to 7000 species of bacteria in just one gram of soil.

Answer:

Both structures have 6 sides.

Answer:

true

Kites and sailboats both use wind to move.

ISBN: 978-1-897457-75-7

The Great Barrier Reef is the world's biggest single structure made by living organisms. How big is it?

A. almost as big as a soccer field

B. so big that it can be seen from outer space

C. bigger than the Pacific Ocean

All except one of the continents have deserts. Which continent does not have a desert?

Asia
Africa
South America
North America
Australia
Antarctica
Europe

Solve the riddle.

My wings are wet.
And this is why
I use them to swim
But not to fly.
What am I?

True or False

Plants can move.

ISBN: 978-1-897457-75-7

Answer:

B. so big that it can be seen from outer space

Answer:

a penguin

Answer:

Europe

Answer:

true

The leaves of a houseplant move to face a window, and sunflowers follow the daily movement of the sun.

ISBN: 978-1-897457-75-7

A stand of five big big oak trees produces 10 000 acorns in the fall. How many of these acorns will become trees?

A. 5000

B. 200

C. 1

Which trail is the best for beginners to ski?

In ancient times, what did people use as spoons?

A. sharp rocks

B. seashells

C. coconut shells

Solve the riddle.

I move fast.
I can touch both the sky
And the ground at the same time.
Some people call me "Twister".
What am I?

ISBN: 978-1-897457-75-7

Answer:

C. 1

Answer:

B. seashells

Seashells were used as spoons and scoops.

Answer:

C

Answer:

a tornado

ISBN: 978-1-897457-75-7